FOUNDATIONS

in PERSONAL FINANCE®

Middle School Edition

ACKNOWLEDGEMENTS

The Ramsey Education Solutions team would like to give special thanks to the following people for their contributions to this product. Their input was essential for creating a financial literacy curriculum that empowers middle school students to make sound financial decisions for life.

EDUCATORS

Linda Bartmess
GUIDANCE COUNSELOR
Whitwell Middle School
Whitwell, Tennessee

Jeffery Baugus
COORDINATOR OF MATH AND SCIENCE
Santa Rosa County School District
Milton, Florida

Nina Bowman
TEACHER
Perry Meridian Middle School
Indianapolis, Indiana

Scott Comstock
SCIENTIFIC COMMUNICATIONS TEACHER
King Middle School
Portland, Maine

Kim Headrick
PRINCIPAL
Whitwell Middle School
Whitwell, Tennessee

Donna Horne
COMMITTEE CHAIR
Boy Scout Troop 413
Dallas, Georgia

Alicia Jobe
TEACHER
Rush Springs Middle School
Rush Springs, Oklahoma

Ted Luke
SCIENCE/PERSONAL FINANCE EDUCATOR
Twentynine Palms Jr. High School
Twentynine Palms, California

Scott Schloesser
6TH GRADE TEACHER
Jackson Middle School
Champlin, Minnesota

Brad Suder
7TH GRADE SOCIAL STUDIES TEACHER
Nagel Middle School
Cincinnati, Ohio

Patrice Thompson
LIFE SKILLS/CAREER TEACHER
Bushland Middle School
Bushland, Texas

David Walters
BUSINESS EDUCATION TEACHER
Eggers Middle School
Hammond, Indiana

Holly Whalen
6TH GRADE SOCIAL STUDIES TEACHER
Heights Middle School
Farmington, New Mexico

CREDITS

Executive Vice President
Jack Galloway

Chief Marketing Officer
Jennifer Sievertsen

Senior Vice President of Education Solutions
Jim King

Curriculum Design
Rick Prall
Michelle Scott

Product Management
Kassidy Slamer
Emily Riser
Ryan Haedge

Marketing/PR
Herb Jenkins
Beth Tallent
Jacqueline Garneau
Rachel Peck

Content Editing/ Proofing
Allen Harris
Jennifer Gingerich
Jason Walter
Emma Berry
Stephanie Thomas

Creative Design
Brian Williams
Jason Miller
Christian Linares

Content Reviewers
Christy Richardson
Kirsten Mickelsen
Nikki Dunaway
Mark Ballinger
Danielle Britt
Ana Daniel
Jess Dever
Jamie Redfearn
Danny Craig
Dennis Palmer
Nate Spencer
Ben Counts
Todd Ward
Julia Waddell
Emily Florek
Kevin Thomas
Molly Pinkley

Video/Audio Production
Jon Melton
Josh Fulton
Dave Oglesby
Diana Gillean
Megan Ledford
Lyndsie Rogers
Jonna Kyle
Chris Wright
Ben Westfall
Ian Collins
Josh Hancock
Dennis Warren

Interactive/Web Development/UI
Jim Ebert
James Ganong
Joel Walden

RACHEL CRUZE

Rachel Cruze is a seasoned communicator, presenter and Ramsey Personality, helping Americans learn the proper ways to handle money and stay out of debt. Her book *Smart Money Smart Kids*, which she co-wrote with her dad, Dave Ramsey, debuted at number one on the *New York Times* best-seller list.

ANTHONY ONEAL

Since 2003, Anthony ONeal has helped thousands of students succeed with money in their work and personal lives. Now Anthony has joined Ramsey Solutions to spread this encouraging message to students nationwide as a Ramsey Personality.

DAVE RAMSEY

America's trusted voice on money and business, Dave has authored seven best-selling books including *The Total Money Makeover* and *Smart Money Smart Kids*. *The Dave Ramsey Show* is heard by more than 12 million listeners each week on more than 575 radio stations.

KEN COLEMAN

An acclaimed interviewer and broadcaster, Ken Coleman is the host of Ramsey Solutions' live events, *The Dave Ramsey Show* Video Channel and the top-rated EntreLeadership Podcast. In 2013, Ken released his first book, *One Question: Life-Changing Answers from Today's Leading Voices*.

MANAGING MONEY GOD'S WAY

Welcome to *Foundations in Personal Finance: Middle School Edition for Homeschool*! In this curriculum, you will gain the tools and knowledge to win with money. But there's more to winning than just understanding the basic principles of money management. What does it look like to handle money God's ways? Many people focus only on giving when they think about honoring God with their money. But handling money and thinking about money in a godly way is about much more than tithing.

MONEY IN THE BIBLE

① PROVERBS 13:22 "A good man leaves an inheritance to his children's children" (NKJV). God wants us to make a difference in our family tree.

② PROVERBS 21:20 "In the house of the wise are stores of choice food and oil, but a foolish man devours all he has" (NIV). This shows us the wisdom of saving for a rainy day and setting something back for safekeeping.

③ PROVERBS 22:7 states that "The rich rule over the poor, and the borrower is slave to the lender" (NIV). The Bible discourages debt.

④ LUKE 14:28 "For which of you, intending to build a tower, does not sit down first and count the cost, whether he has enough to finish it" (NKJV). The Bible teaches us to save up and pay for the things we buy.

⑤ MATTHEW 6:24 "You cannot serve both God and money" (NIV). God wants your attention focused on Him alone.

The Bible tells us that we're stewards of God's resources. By definition, a steward is not an owner, but a manager—someone who takes care of the possessions of someone else.

When we believe that God is the owner of all we have, we gain a new perspective on how we handle the resources we have been given. When you choose to handle money God's ways, things that used to be difficult will become easier. Budgeting, compromising, saving, giving, sacrificing, making wiser decisions with your money—all of it will become clearer.

CONTENTS

A
budget
tells
your money
where
to go!

01

Saving & Budgeting

The road map for your money.

73% of teens consider themselves "super savers" as opposed to "big spenders"[1]

83% of teens admit they don't know much about personal finance[2]

> Today, there are three kinds of people: the haves, the have-nots, and the have-not-paid-for-what-they-haves.

EARL WILSON, American columnist

> Of the billionaires I have known, money just brings out the basic traits in them. If they were jerks before they had money, they are simply jerks with a billion dollars.

WARREN BUFFETT, entrepreneur and philanthropist

> The plans of the diligent lead surely to plenty, but those of everyone who is hasty, surely to poverty.

PROVERBS 21:5 NKJV

I Can...

LESSON 1

☐ Describe what it means to be financially responsible.

☐ Recognize the difference between assets and liabilities.

☐ Explain the meaning of net worth.

LESSON 2

☐ Describe how saving money improves my financial well-being.

☐ Identify three basic reasons for saving money.

☐ Compare simple interest and compound interest.

LESSON 3

☐ Understand the difference between wants and needs.

☐ Describe the difference between a credit card and a debit card.

☐ Explain how to balance a checkbook or bank statement.

LESSON 4

☐ Recognize my money personality.

☐ Understand how to talk about money with family members.

☐ Describe different types of expenses.

LESSON 5

☐ Identify my core values.

☐ Explain the meaning of charitable giving.

☐ Describe the benefits of giving.

Asset: Anything of value that is owned by an individual

Budget: A monthly plan for how you are going to save and spend your income

Compound Interest: Interest paid on an investment and on any interest previously earned

Consumer: A person or organization that purchases a product or service

Credit: The granting of a loan and the creation of debt

Debt: An obligation to repay borrowed money

Expense: The cost of goods or services

Interest: The charge for borrowed money generally defined as a percentage; also, the earned interest on money you save or invest

Investments: Money put into an account intended for growth

Liability: Anything you owe; a debt

Net Worth: The total value of a person's assets (things owned) minus their liabilities (things owed); may be a positive or negative dollar amount

Nonprofit Organization: A federally recognized, tax-exempt organization such as a church, hospital, charity, or school that serves the public in some capacity

Personal Finance: All the money decisions a person or family makes including earning, budgeting, saving, spending, and planning for the future

Simple Interest: Interest paid only on the principal investment

Scarcity: An unlimited amount of wants but limited resources

Get Smart with Money

Personal finance includes everything you do with money.

LESSON 1

MONEY 101

Personal finance simply means how you handle your money. It refers to all the money choices a person or family must make in order to earn, **budget**, save, and spend money—as well as plan for emergencies and for the future.

Most people view money as simply a way to get something they want. When you get money, you probably spend it without putting too much thought into what you are buying. But it won't be long before the way you spend money will impact your financial security in the future.

The Five Foundations are the beginner steps for establishing and maintaining financial peace. These are basic steps that any teenager can and should follow in order to win with money.

THE 5 FOUNDATIONS

 $500 FIRST FOUNDATION
Save a $500 emergency fund

 SECOND FOUNDATION
Get out of debt

 THIRD FOUNDATION
Pay cash for your first car

 FOURTH FOUNDATION
Pay cash for college

 FIFTH FOUNDATION
Build wealth and give

 If you had the money to buy whatever you wanted, what would you buy right now? Why?

MONEY-SMART

Personal finance is about 80% _____,
and it's only 20% _____ _____.

Becoming money-smart involves four things:

_____, _____,
_____, and give.

DEBT IS EXPENSIVE

You might think most people are doing pretty well when it comes to money. They drive new cars, live in big houses, and wear nice clothes. The truth is that most people are living paycheck to paycheck. They run out of money from their last paycheck before they get their next paycheck.

To fill this money gap, many Americans borrow money—or use **credit**. Just because someone appears rich doesn't mean they have a lot of money. People can have really nice stuff and not be rich. It can all be purchased on credit, and that creates a huge pile of **debt**.

Debt is _____ _____ to
anyone for any reason.

JOURNAL QUESTION

Describe a time when you spent your money on something and later wished you had used the money for something else.

_____

_____

_____

_____

What's Net Worth?

To win with money, you'll need to learn the language of money. One of the terms to understand is **net worth**, which is basically how much money a person, family, or business can claim as total value. Your net worth is figured by subtracting all of your **liabilities** (the things you owe, including any debt) from the value of all of your **assets** (the things you own and the money you have).

For Example

Jose and Julia want to determine their net worth. They are paying a mortgage on their home. Jose drives a four-year-old truck, and Julia drives a twelve-year-old car. They have some money in the bank, but they both owe on student loans and credit cards. They have the following assets (value in blue) and liabilities (debt in grey).

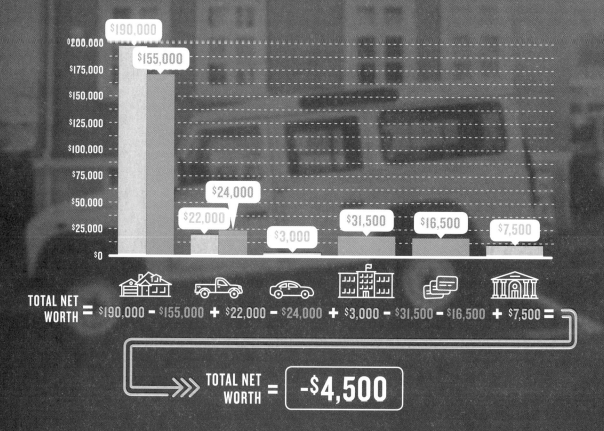

TOTAL NET WORTH = $190,000 − $155,000 + $22,000 − $24,000 + $3,000 − $31,500 − $16,500 + $7,500 =

TOTAL NET WORTH = **−$4,500**

Personal Finance Basics

Studying the topic of personal finance is your first step to winning with money. There are a lot of words and concepts to know when you talk about personal finance. Understanding these different terms and phrases will help you make wise choices when it comes to your money. Let's get started!

DIRECTIONS: Match the following terms with the correct descriptions.

A debt   **D** behavior   **G** The First Foundation

B personal finance   **E** net worth   **H** knowledge

C The Five Foundations **F** liabilities   **I** assets

---

1. _____ Save a $500 emergency fund.

2. _____ Owing anything to anyone.

3. _____ The things you do with money.

4. _____ The things you own.

5. _____ The financial peace beginner steps.

6. _____ All things related to money.

7. _____ What you know about money.

8. _____ The things you owe.

9. _____ The value of one's assets minus liabilities.

- -

FINAL THOUGHT: In the house of the wise are stores of choice food and oil, but a foolish man devours all he has.
PROVERBS 21:20 NIV 84

Cash in the Bank

Saving and investing are wealth-building basics.

SUPER SAVING

Saving money is important, and it is one of the basic steps to building wealth. Saving gives you options when you're ready to buy things, and it gives you peace of mind. When you are young and only have access to small amounts of money, it may seem impossible to set some of it aside for saving. However, if you establish this habit early in life, it will become easier for you. Saving money will also prevent you from going into debt when unexpected wants or needs arise!

> Whenever you receive money as a gift or for work, take _____ _____ ____ and put it away for savings.

THREE REASONS TO SAVE

> There are three basic reasons to save money: Emergency Fund, _____, and Wealth Building.

Emergency Fund: This is extra cash to use when things come up that you weren't expecting. Money emergencies will happen. Many people end up going into debt to cover these expenses. But with an emergency fund, you have the cash to cover them.

Purchases: This money is saved to purchase things you want like a shirt, a concert ticket, or even a car. It's important to save up and pay cash for these things instead of buying them on credit and going into debt.

Interest on credit is a _____ you pay on top of the money you already _____.

⏱ What is one purchase you want to start saving for?

Wealth Building: Did you know that your money can earn you more money? That's really exciting! The common term for this is **investments**. This includes any money that you put in the bank that earns interest. When you invest money, you earn interest rather than pay it, and that's always a good thing.

Investments are things that are purchased with an expectation that they will grow in _____ or produce _____ over time.

Money that's invested can earn simple or compound interest—basically the math that makes your money grow. **Simple interest** is just added to your initial investment, also called the principal. Compound interest is a mathematical explosion that helps you build wealth! **Compound interest** is added to your principal *and* to the previous interest you earned. And it just keeps growing!

JOURNAL QUESTION

Explain how saving a portion of your money can help you achieve financial well-being.

— APPLY WHAT YOU'VE LEARNED —

Saving Up

Budgeting involves figuring out how long it will take to save for purchases based on how much money you typically earn or receive in a week or a month.

DIRECTIONS: Figure out how many weeks it would take you to save up and pay cash for the following items:

1. _____ Online song download ($1.30)

2. _____ Ice cream ($4.50)

3. _____ Fast-food meal ($8.50)

4. _____ New T-shirt ($13.00)

5. _____ Online movie download ($15.00)

6. _____ Going to a movie with snacks and a drink ($19.00)

7. _____ New jeans ($29.50)

8. _____ New hoodie ($35.00)

9. _____ Video game ($60.00)

10. _____ Athletic shoes ($119.00)

11. _____ New cell phone ($199.00–299.00)

12. _____ New tablet or laptop ($400.00–900.00)

FINAL THOUGHT: Ants are creatures of little strength, yet they store up their food in the summer.

PROVERBS 30:25 NIV

A Money Plan

A budget is a plan that tells your money where to go.

NEEDS AND WANTS

Needs are things you _____ to have.

Wants are fun but not _____

to survive.

Understanding the difference between wants and needs can be tricky. But being a smart consumer means you can make smart choices about how you spend your money. As a **consumer**, you need to realize that people often have unlimited wants but limited resources (money). This is called **scarcity**. With a limited amount of money, you need to plan to cover all of your needs before you start spending money on any of your wants. Identify the following items as needs or wants:

☐ NEED ☐ WANT   ☐ NEED ☐ WANT   ☐ NEED ☐ WANT

☐ NEED ☐ WANT   ☐ NEED ☐ WANT   ☐ NEED ☐ WANT

A SPENDING PLAN

It's important to have a _____ for what you're going to do with your money.

So how do you know if you are managing your money well? Now is a great time to start keeping a record of your spending. It's easy! When you earn money, simply write down the total amount of money you have, then list the items you buy and how much they cost. Having a plan is the best way to manage your money.

This plan for your money is called a _____.

TYPES OF EXPENSES

Writing a **budget** helps you give every dollar a name and an assignment before the month begins. Remember, a budget is your spending plan for any bills you have to pay as well as the thing you will buy. There are four types of expenses you'll need to know about when you develop your monthly budget.

① **Variable Expenses:** change in dollar amount every month and include things like utility bills, gasoline, and groceries.

② **Fixed Expenses:** remain the same from month to month like rent and insurance premiums.

③ **Discretionary Expenses:** for things you don't necessarily need like eating out, gifts, and candy.

④ **Intermittent Expenses:** occur at different times throughout the year and tend to be in large lump sums like tuition payments and car repairs.

✎ 36% of teen girls say they save money to buy music or clothing.[3]

✎ 48% of teen guys say they save money to buy technology and computer items.[4]

A bank account is a big deal. With your money in the bank, you have the ability to spend it with a debit card or a check. Just remember to keep up with how much you spend when you buy something.

Banks will offer you debit cards as well as credit cards. So, what's the difference between a debit card and a credit card? They may look the same, but there is a big difference in how they work.

A debit card only allows you to use the money you _____ _____ in the bank.

Using a credit card means you _____ _____ to buy stuff.

Remember, winning with money means avoiding debt! Stay away from credit cards. A debit card can be used for anything you would use a credit card for—and you won't spend money you don't have! Credit cards allow you to borrow the money, but then the credit card company charges you interest on your balance. And here is something else to consider: Surveys show that people spend more money using a credit card than they do when using cash.[5]

JOURNAL QUESTION

In addition to saving money, what are some other ways you can show financial responsibility?

_____

_____

_____

_____

Debit Cards vs. Credit Cards

Debit Cards[6]	Credit Cards[7]
590+ million cards in US circulation	507+ million cards in US circulation
You only spend money you already have	You borrow money and create debt
No interest penalty on purchases	Average annual interest rate is 13%
63% of people use a debit card to purchase groceries	33% of people miss payments and have to pay late fees
Average personal debt using a debit card: $0	Average personal debt using a credit card: $4,878

There's a common misconception that debit cards have some limitations, but that's simply not true. A debit card will allow you to do all of the things a credit card will do, such as:

 Make purchases in a store

 Make purchases online

 Eat at a restaurant

 Rent a car

 Buy a plane ticket

 Reserve a hotel room

 Buy a concert ticket

 And, a VISA debit card has the same protections as a VISA credit card

Here's one thing a debit card won't do: put you into debt!

— APPLY WHAT YOU'VE LEARNED —

A Balanced Approach

If you want to win with money, it's really important to learn how to keep track of your purchases, withdrawals, transfers, and deposits. Poor record keeping and mistakes can cost you a lot of money in the form of overdraft fees (often listed as NSF fees: Non-Sufficient Funds). These fees happen when you think you've got more money in your account than you actually do. Your bank will subtract this fee directly from your account.

DIRECTIONS: For the following case studies, subtract all the debit card purchases and monthly bills from each person's paycheck deposits. Determine how much money each person has available in their account.

1. Before getting paid, Brian had a balance of $250 in his checking account. He then received his paycheck of $1,150 by direct deposit. His rent is $650, and his utilities are $50. He bought $300 worth of groceries. He went to the movie theater to watch the latest release and spent $20 on his movie ticket, popcorn, and a drink. He spent $40 on gas for his car and bought $100 worth of clothes at the mall.

   How much money does Brian have left? _____

   _____

   _____

2. Before getting paid, Lindsey had a balance of $10 in her bank account. She then received her paycheck for $900. Her car payment is $350, and she spent $60 on gas. She bought $150 worth of groceries, then gave her portion of the rent and utilities—$300—to her roommate.

   How much money does Lindsey have left? _____

   _____

   _____

- -

FINAL THOUGHT: If riches increase, do not set your heart on them.

PSALM 62:10 NKJV

Money Matters

Communication can help you avoid money fights.

SPENDERS AND SAVERS

It has been said that money makes the world go 'round. Just about everything in the world requires money—travel, entertainment, food, services, supplies, electricity. All the buying and selling that goes on is tied to money. As you learn about money and develop some skills in the areas of **personal finance**, it's also important to become familiar with your own money personality.

Savers will naturally _____ money.

Spenders will naturally _____ money.

It is important to _____ if you are a saver or a spender.

For some people, having money in the bank is more important than having the newest cell phone, while other people really have to work to save money and keep their spending in check. Whether you are a natural saver or a natural spender, you need to know that your money personality is neither good nor bad. Being aware of your money personality will help you create a money plan that works for you. When you create your budget, include both saving and spending.

 Is your best friend a saver or a spender? How do you know?

MONEY TALK

Talking about money, especially with family members, can cause conflict if you expect others to view money the same way you do. Once you understand that people relate to money in a variety of ways, you can learn to respect those differences. When it comes to money, communication is important and necessary. Here are some practical tips:

» **Pick the right time and place.** Starting a money conversation two minutes before it's time to leave for work or school or when it is time for bed is not ideal. Make sure there is plenty of time to have a relaxed and complete conversation.

» **Be willing to work.** When you need some extra money, your willingness to work can go a long way toward meeting your goal.

» **Talk about your money goals.** Let others close to you know about your financial goals. This will help provide accountability and encouragement along the way.

» **Listen.** Communicating isn't just about expressing your own needs and wants. It's also about listening to what others need and want.

» **Be honest.** When it comes to money and relationships, honesty is key.

FOUR FINANCIAL TOPICS

Remember, personal finance involves everything you do with money. This important topic includes how you go about making money and how you use money.

» **Work:** The ways you earn money.

» **Spend:** How you spend money.

» **Save:** Planning to use money later for purchases and wealth building.

» **Give:** Offering your money, time, talent, and abilities to serve others.

JOURNAL QUESTION

Based on what you've learned about saving and budgeting, how will you handle money you receive in the future?

_____

_____

_____

_____

Saving and Spending: By the Numbers

SAVING

77%
of teens consider themselves savers

53%
of teens have a savings account

On average . . .

. . . teens save $300 per year

. . . teens have saved $966 total

Why Teens Save

76% save for college

46% save for an emergency

43% save for bigger purchases

41% save for a car

Where Teens Get Their Money

67% from a job of some type

59% from gifts

34% from a weekly allowance

10% from selling items/clothing

See Chapter 1 endnote source citations 8, 9, 10.

SPENDING

23%
of teens consider themselves spenders

28%
of teens owe money to someone
($252 on average)

On average . . .

. . . teens spend 20% of their money on food

. . . teens spend $1,000 per year on fashion goods

What Teens Buy

84% of teens own a cell phone

76% of teens own an MP3 player

66% of teens own a computer

46% of teens own a TV

Where Teens Shop Online

1. Amazon (32%)

2. Nike (8%)

3. eBay (5%)

4. Forever 21 (5%)

— APPLY WHAT YOU'VE LEARNED —

Saver or Spender?

Are you a spender or a saver? Knowing your money personality can help you manage your budget wisely. This simple quiz can help you figure out (if you don't know already) if you are a spender or a saver.

DIRECTIONS: Circle the statements that best describe you when it comes to money.

1. You would rather not spend $5.25 on specialty ice cream at the local shop when you can buy a quart of it at the grocery store for less than that.

2. You have $1.50 in your pocket—just enough for another soft drink from a vending machine. Score!

3. You think that saving money is much more fun than spending money.

4. When you get birthday money, you save it for something you want to buy when you have enough money.

5. You are at your favorite store and that new T-shirt looks great so you buy it.

6. The terms "tightwad" or "cheapskate" or "penny pincher" are often used to describe you.

7. The first thing you do when you get birthday money is head to the store to spend it.

8. Your savings envelope always has money in it.

9. The phrase "money burns a hole in your pocket" is often used to describe you.

10. You know exactly how much money you have saved.

11. When you go shopping, you buy things because they look good.

12. You would rather spend a little more money now to get what your really want right away.

13. When you have extra money, you would rather save it than spend it.

14. You generally feel that if you have money, you should spend it.

NOW, HOW MANY OF THESE STATEMENTS DID YOU CIRCLE?

1, 3, 4, 6, 8, 10, 13 _____ = Saver   2, 5, 7, 9, 11, 12, 14 _____ = Spender

Are you more of a spender or a saver? _____

- -

FINAL THOUGHT: A faithful man will abound with blessings, but he who hastens to be rich will not go unpunished.
PROVERBS 28:20 NKJV

Giving to Others

It's hard to be selfish when you're giving to others.

SELFIE NATION

"Me. It's all about me." Everyone seems to be focused on themselves: *How do I look? How do I feel? What can I buy for myself? What makes me happy? What can others do for me?* It all feels rather selfish, don't you think? We live in a "selfie" culture where giving to others is not at the top of most people's list of things to do.

people are not fun to be around.

₂₂

No, every person isn't selfish or greedy. But let's face it, the act of giving isn't always the first thing people think about.

The tragedy is that this type of attitude robs people of the experience and joy that comes from giving to others.

When you become the opposite of selfish, you become _____ .

₂₃

BEING CHARITABLE

Charitable giving is generally defined as giving money to a **nonprofit organization** like churches, hospitals, charities, and schools. These types of organizations usually rely on donations from others in order to operate. Also, they use the money they receive to further their mission and serve others.

 What is your favorite thing you have done for someone else?

Remember, there are three things you can do with money: spend, save, and give. Giving to others is important and a lot of fun. Obviously, if someone needs money to buy food and you give them money, they are able to eat. But giving goes beyond just giving away your money. You may not have a lot of money right now, but that doesn't mean you don't have anything to give. Whether you have a little or have a lot, you can give of your time, talents, and abilities to help others.

You can give by giving of your _____.

₂₄

Giving to others makes them feel good because you were willing to give—whether it was money or time. But giving also benefits you as the giver. You feel happy because you focused on others and did something for someone else. Also, giving has been shown to be good for your health. When you give to others, it connects you with other people and produces gratitude for things you already have. And giving is contagious—when you give, it causes others to do the same.

JOURNAL QUESTION

Describe a time when you were able to do something for someone else. How did this make you feel?

_____

_____

_____

When you invest your time, you make a goal and a decision of something that you want to accomplish. Whether it's make good grades in school, be a good athlete, be a good person, go down and do some community service and help somebody who's in need, whatever it is you choose to do, you're investing your time in that.

NICK SABAN, college football coach

How Can We Help Others?

Here are some ideas for how you can give of your free time or breaks from school—and they don't require money:

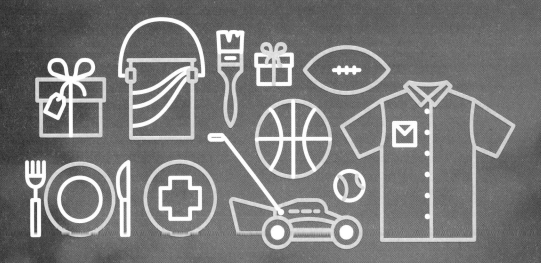

» Painting an elderly neighbor's house.

» Helping with a recreation program for little kids after school.

» Serving others on a mission trip with your church.

» Volunteering your time to help feed and care for the homeless.

» Babysitting for a single mom for free.

» Mowing someone's yard for free when they are sick.

» Donating some of your extra clothes to a family who lost everything in a house fire.

» Collecting new or lightly used toys to deliver to a children's hospital.

— APPLY WHAT YOU'VE LEARNED —

Your Core Values

A core value is something that is really important to you—something you make a priority. If being generous is important to you, you will find it easier to give to others. When you give to others, make sure that you focus on something that is really important to you. If you are passionate about it, you will be motivated to make a difference in the situation. Knowing the things that you value will help you find an organization or charity or service project that fits you.

DIRECTIONS: Circle the ten qualities that are most important to you from the list below.

respectful	leader	humorous	intellect
trustworthy	compassionate	honest	assertive
spiritual	accountable	patient	cooperative
forgiving	peaceful	committed	creative
confident	loyal	energetic	persistent
loving	accepting	helpful	fair
hardworking	sensitive	self-controlled	unifying
giving	kind	excellence	competitive
unique	joyful	communication	gentle

NOW LIST YOUR TOP 3: These are the qualities you value the most—your core values.

1. _____   2. _____   3. _____

- -

FINAL THOUGHT: God loves a cheerful giver.

2 CORINTHIANS 9:7 NKJV

Recap & Review

WHAT CAN YOU DO NOW?

 It's time to check your learning! Go back to the "I Can" statements at the beginning of this chapter. Place a check mark next to each statement that you can now do.

ILLUSTRATION TIME

Draw a picture representation of the following terms.

Liabilities

Emergency Fund

MONEY IN REVIEW

Circle the correct answer.

1. A liability can be described as:
- **A** Something that goes down in value over time
- **B** Money that you have in a savings account
- **C** Money you owe; a debt
- **D** Something you own that has value

2. A measurement of the total dollar value of one's assets minus liabilities.
- **A** Wealth
- **B** Earnings
- **C** Income
- **D** Net worth

3. Which of the following allows invested money to grow over time?
- **A** Premium payments
- **B** Taxes
- **C** Compound interest
- **D** Inflation

4. A plan for spending is called a(n):
- **A** Account
- **B** Budget
- **C** Economy
- **D** Scarcity

5. The condition of having unlimited wants but limited resources is known as:
- **A** Scarcity
- **B** Consumerism
- **C** Global demand
- **D** Budgeting

6. Refers to all the financial decisions an individual or family must make in order to earn, budget, save, and spend money over time.
- **A** Financial aid
- **B** Personal finance
- **C** Home finance
- **D** Cash-flow statement

Debt is a monster that will destroy your financial plan.

02

Credit & Debt

Avoid dangerous money traps.

68% of all American consumers have one or more credit cards.[1]

60% of college seniors graduate with a credit card and a debt balance.[2]

> Credit is a system whereby a person who cannot pay gets another person who cannot pay to guarantee that he can pay.

CHARLES DICKENS, writer and novelist

> Rather go to bed supperless than rise in debt.

BENJAMIN FRANKLIN, author, inventor, and scientist

> The rich rule over the poor, and the borrower is slave to the lender.

PROVERBS 22:7 NIV

I Can...

LESSON 1

☐ Define loan, debt, and credit.

☐ Describe the use of credit in America.

☐ Analyze the financial impact of debt on a household budget.

LESSON 2

☐ Recognize some of the "debt myths" that exist today.

☐ Describe the dangers of debt.

☐ Compare the cost difference between cash and credit.

LESSON 3

☐ Explain what makes up a credit score.

☐ Describe what a debt collector is.

LESSON 4

☐ Evaluate the effects of taking on debt to fund my college education.

☐ Understand ways to pay for college without going into debt.

☐ Explain the long-term cost of student loan debt.

Car Loan: A short-term, personal loan to purchase a car; monthly payments with interest are made over time (72 months)

Credit Card: A plastic card used to buy good or services using debt

Credit Score: An assigned number to signal to lenders a person's ability to repay a loan

Debt Collector: Someone who collects debts owed to others

Grant: Financial aid that does not need to be repaid; generally based on financial need

Interest: The charge for borrowed money generally defined as a percentage; also, the earned interest on money you save or invest

Lender: A person or company who loans money

Scholarship: Financial aid that does not need to be repaid; awarded on the basis of academic, athletic, achievement, or other criteria

Student Loan: Educational loan at a lower interest rate generally with no payments until after you are out of school

Work Study: A program that allows students to work part-time while in college

 Our great-grandparents thought debt was a sin. Our grandparents thought debt was dumb. Our parents borrowed on a few things. We borrow on everything.

DAVE RAMSEY

Credit Concerns

Debt is owing anything to anyone for any reason.

LESSON 1

THE DEBT MONSTER

One part of dealing with money that gets people into trouble is debt. The Second Foundation is to get out of debt—and stay out of debt. Remember, debt is owing anything to anyone for any reason. Too many families find themselves living paycheck to paycheck because of debt. When you borrow money, you have to pay it back with **interest**. Interest is a fee that a bank, credit card company, or other **lender** charges so that you can purchase something and pay for it over time.

> Whether it's credit cards, student loans, or car loans, going into debt is always a _____ idea.

> Save up and pay for things you want with _____ and say NO to debt.

SELLING DEBT

All of the interest payments that go along with car loans, student loans, and credit cards create huge problems for people. If debt causes so many problems, then why do people use debt so often? There are many reasons, but a big one is:

> Debt is _____ to us just like any other product.

Debt is marketed a lot like how cereal, candy, and smartphone apps are marketed. You don't have to watch TV long before you see and hear the marketing of debt:

"Just five easy payments of $19.95!"

"30 days same as cash!"

"Zero down and 0% interest for 12 months!"

"No payments until next year!"

How do you know if you can afford to buy something? Here's the answer: if you have the cash to pay for it! If you don't have the cash right now, then you should wait and save up for it. Don't fall for the marketing traps that will lead you into debt. Be careful, because debt can make people look better-off than they really are! Remember, having nice stuff doesn't mean someone has a lot of money.

 What is your favorite TV commercial? What is it selling?

THE IMPACT OF DEBT

One of the biggest money mistakes people make is going into debt. Do you want something now but don't have the money to buy it? No problem! Just put it on a little plastic card and worry about paying for it later. (Hint: That's a bad idea!) But that one little want quickly turns into a lot of wants—a new coat, a new phone, a new computer, and a new car!

You've probably seen a few credit card commercials on TV or have seen other people using credit cards. Keep in mind that debt and interest payments stack up until you have a huge pile of your hard-earned money going back out the door in payments. And that means you won't be able to do or buy other things. Debt eats up a lot of people's money every month.

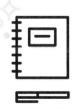 JOURNAL QUESTION
When have you seen debt cause financial problems for adults you know? What can you do to avoid these financial problems when you are an adult?

_____

_____

_____

_____

The Impact of Debt

Debt is a huge problem. Statistically, the average family sends almost 25% of their hard-earned money back out in payments (often minimum monthly payments) to lenders for credit card purchases, student loans, and car loans.[3]

So, if the average family earned $4,000 per month, how much would they send back out to pay debt each month?

$_____

What kinds of things could you do with that money?

_____

_____

_____

Now, imagine this same family earned twice as much money—$8,000 per month. But let's say they still keep up their credit card purchases and are still sending 25% of their money back to debt payments. How much would that be per month?

$_____

What kinds of things could you do with that money?

_____

_____

_____

- -

FINAL THOUGHT: He who walks with the wise grows wise, but a companion of fools suffers harm.

PROVERBS 13:20 NIV 84

The Dangers of Debt

Debt will suck the life out of your financial plan.

DEBT MYTHS

When you imagine your life as a young adult, it probably includes a driver's license and a **credit card**. While a driver's license is good and a necessary tool in life, a credit card is not. We want to help you avoid learning the ugly truth about debt the hard way. Here are three money myths you need to understand:

Myth: You need to have a _____ _____.

Truth: A debit card will do everything a credit card will do—except put you into debt! Why? Because a debit card uses money you have in your account. You don't need a credit card and you certainly don't need the debt that goes with it.

Myth: _____ _____ are a way of life, and you'll always have a car payment.

Truth: Staying away from car payments by driving reliable used cars is what the typical millionaire does. That is how they became millionaires. You don't need to have a **car loan** in order to drive a car. You can, and should, pay cash for a car.

Myth: _____ is fun because I can buy whatever I want.

Truth: When you owe money to others, you can't continue to buy whatever you want because your money is used to pay debt. While buying things may be a lot of fun, having to pay for them for a long time is no fun—and it gets expensive.

If you had the cash to buy any car you wanted, what would be your dream car?

CASH OR CREDIT

Paying with cash means you can buy something right away if you have the money. Buying something on credit also allows you to buy something right away.

But, if you use credit, you will have something to pay later. Your payments will stretch out over time and include even more money when you add interest.

> If you pay with cash, you won't have to worry about
> _____ anything else later.

For example, let's say you really want the latest running shoes. Your favorite store has the shoes on sale for $100. If you paid cash, how much would you pay? $100 (And you might even get an extra discount with cash if you ask.).

If you use the store credit card and just make the $10 minimum monthly payments, how much would you pay? With interest, you would pay $110 and it would take you eleven months. More than likely, the shoes would be worn out by then.

 JOURNAL QUESTION

How would you describe the dangers of debt to a friend?

_____

_____

_____

_____

 86% of teens say they would rather learn about money management in a class before making mistakes in the real world.'

— APPLY WHAT YOU'VE LEARNED —

The Cost of Credit

Your favorite store offers a credit card with a 20% annual interest rate (1.7% per month). For larger purchases, most credit cards charge 3% of your balance or a monthly minimum payment ($10/month on this card), whichever may be higher. The cost of credit is magnified when your purchases get bigger. For example, if you used the store credit card to purchase $1,000 worth of stuff (like a new laptop) and just made the minimum monthly payments, the chart below shows what your first year of payments would look like:[5]

DIRECTIONS: Calculate how much you paid in total after a year of making the minimum monthly payments. Also, calculate how much you paid in interest payments after a year.

Month	Minimum Payment	Principal Paid	Interest Paid	Remaining Balance
1	$30.00	$13.33	$16.67	$986.67
2	$28.60	$13.16	$16.44	$973.51
3	$29.21	$12.98	$16.23	$960.53
4	$28.82	$12.81	$16.01	$947.73
5	$28.43	$12.63	$15.80	$935.10
6	$28.05	$12.47	$15.58	$922.62
7	$27.68	$12.30	$15.38	$910.33
8	$27.31	$12.14	$15.17	$898.19
9	$26.95	$11.98	$14.97	$886.21
10	$26.59	$11.82	$14.77	$874.39
11	$26.23	$11.66	$14.57	$862.73
12	$25.88	$11.50	$14.38	$851.23
Total:	$ _____	$148.78	$ _____	

KEEP IN MIND: This is just for the first year of your payments. In this example, it would take you 131 months (over 10.5 years!) to pay off the $1,000 purchase if you just made the minimum payments! And, your total interest payments would be $991 making your total cost $1,991! That's quite a difference between paying with cash versus credit!

- -

FINAL THOUGHT: Owe no one anything except to love one another.

ROMANS 13:8 NKJV

The Truth about Credit Scores

A credit score is really an "I love debt" score.

CREDIT SCORES AND REPORTS

You will hear people talk about **credit scores** and credit reports. Remember, when you hear the word *credit*, it is referring to debt—and debt is bad. So what is a credit score? Credit reporting companies keep track of all your debt including student loans, credit cards, and other loans (such as a home mortgage loan). These reports indicate how often you are late or on time with your debt payments. Companies use that information to give you a credit score that represents your credit risk—or how likely it is that you will repay your debt.

> Basically, your credit score is an "I love _____" score.

> A "good" credit report or a high credit score doesn't mean you have a lot of money or you are good with money. It just means you have _____.

Credit scores aren't used to show how well you handle money. They simply measure your interaction with debt. Your score often determines how willing a store or lender will be to extend credit to you and allow you to make payments on a purchase. They want to know how likely you are to pay what you owe.

How Is a FICO Score Calculated?

When most people think of a **credit score**, they generally think of the FICO score. The FICO score is one of the ways credit scores are measured, and FICO is simply the name of a company that computes those scores. The company, started in the 1950s, was originally named Fair Isaac Corporation after its two founders, William Fair and Earl Isaac, and in 2009, it changed its name to FICO. Other companies, such as Equifax, Transunion, and Experian, also compute credit scores.

The truth is that the FICO score is an "I love debt" score. In fact, according to their website, 100% of the score is based on your debt, not your wealth. It has nothing to do with your savings, your income, or your investments. And items that appear on your credit report—good and bad—will remain there for 7–10 years or more.

Components of a FICO Score

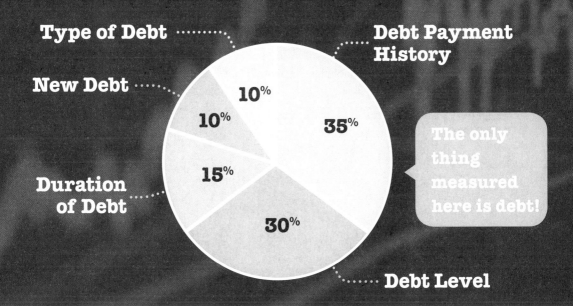

Type of Debt ······· 10%

New Debt ······· 10%

Duration of Debt ······· 15%

Debt Payment History ······· 35%

Debt Level ······· 30%

The only thing measured here is debt!

CONSUMER CREDIT LAW

In 1970, the US Congress enacted the Fair Credit Reporting Act (FCRA) to protect consumers and their credit reports. The FCRA protects consumers in three main ways: 1) The accuracy of a credit report—if something is inaccurate, you can have it changed; 2) The privacy of the consumer—a person or organization needs a good reason to check your credit report; 3) The fairness of credit reporting—if you are denied credit, you must be told why. In addition, the FCRA allows people to receive one free copy of their credit report per year. Everyone should check their credit report each year to identify any mistakes and have them corrected.

STEPS OUT OF DEBT

As you get older, we hope you will remember learning about the dangers of debt and avoid it throughout your life. Saving money so you can pay with cash will help you avoid debt. But if you—or someone you know—end up struggling with debt, here are some steps to help you get rid of it:

① Quit borrowing more money!

② You must save money.

③ Sell something.

④ Get a part-time job or work extra.

⑤ Use the debt snowball method to pay off debts smallest to largest.

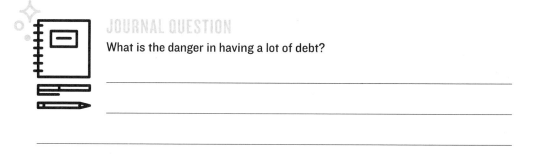

JOURNAL QUESTION

What is the danger in having a lot of debt?

_____

_____

_____

_____

> A hundred wagon loads of thoughts will not pay a single ounce of debt.
>
> **ITALIAN PROVERB**

— APPLY WHAT YOU'VE LEARNED —

Fair or Unfair?

The Federal Fair Debt Collection Practices Act of 1977 dictates how **debt collectors** can interact with individuals. For example, by law they are only able to call you between the hours of 8 a.m. and 9 p.m. They can't call you at work unless you agree to that. They can't call your neighbors or relatives and embarrass you in front of them. Most of the law related to how debt collectors can go about collecting debt from you actually involves common sense and treating people correctly.

DIRECTIONS: Label each of the following as either Fair or Unfair practices of debt collectors based on the paragraph above and what you would consider fair ways to treat people.

1. Calling and yelling at you at 11 p.m. ☐ FAIR ☐ UNFAIR

2. Calling your father and telling him how much you owe ☐ FAIR ☐ UNFAIR

3. Threatening that you will go to jail if you don't pay your debt ☐ FAIR ☐ UNFAIR

4. Discussing a repayment schedule and putting it in writing ☐ FAIR ☐ UNFAIR

5. Calling you at work during the day, after you told them not to ☐ FAIR ☐ UNFAIR

6. Using profanity and threats to make you pay ☐ FAIR ☐ UNFAIR

- -

FINAL THOUGHT: The wicked borrow and do not repay.

PSALM 37:21 NIV

The High Cost of Student Loans

Without a plan, you'll pay for college for a long time.

GOING TO COLLEGE

The earlier you begin thinking about college, the better off you will be. Why? Because going to college can be expensive! You will be offered **student loans** because our culture thinks student loan debt is normal or even "good debt." The fact is there is no type of debt that is good debt—especially student loan debt!

 If you could go to any college, where would you want to go and why?

THE IMPACT OF DEBT ON YOUR EDUCATION

Paying for college probably isn't even on your radar. Later, taking out a loan to pay for school may not seem like such a big deal. Everyone is going to tell you that's the only way to go to college. But, student loan debt can influence a variety of choices in your post-college life and chain you to a huge pile of student loan debt.

Student loans can _____ your options on what you want to do in your life.

The total student loan debt in the United States is over $1 trillion! That is "trillion" with a "T"—a one followed by twelve zeros! Over 70% of any college graduating class graduates with student loan debt and makes payments for ten to thirty years.[6]

Stay away from _____ _____.

PAYING FOR COLLEGE

The good news is that you can go to college without student loans. That's right! Now, it's not easy to pay cash for college. You will need to plan ahead, make smart decisions about where to go to school, and get a job. But it can be done.

Choose a school you can _____.

This may seem like a huge blow to your vision of a carefree college lifestyle; however, the sacrifices you make when you're young will have huge payoffs later. Some choices you make now can make it much more affordable to go to college:

» Community colleges are a great way to keep costs down.

» In-state schools cost less than going to college out of state.

» Plan to work at least part time while you are in school.

» Good grades now will prepare you for the ACT and SAT tests and help you earn **scholarships** and **grants** for college.

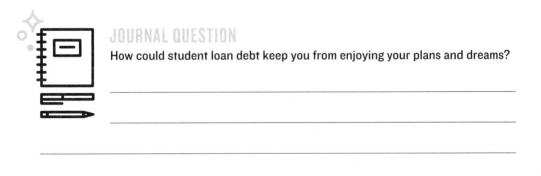

JOURNAL QUESTION

How could student loan debt keep you from enjoying your plans and dreams?

_____

_____

_____

_____

% 76% of teens say they are saving money for college.[7]

% 65% of teens say their parents talk with them about the cost of college.[8]

A Loan-Free College Experience

Can you pay for college without taking out student loans? Yes!
Some ways to pay for college without student loans include:

Scholarships

Scholarships are financial aid offers based on academics, athletics,
achievements, and a variety of other criteria. Scholarships are the
best, safest, and most cost-effective way to pay for college. This is
free money that does not need to be repaid. You will have to fill out
some applications, write some essays, demonstrate athletic skill, or
do well on testing. There are hundreds of different scholarships for
which you can apply. Just do some research. When it comes to
testing, the higher you score on the ACT or SAT, the more
scholarships you will qualify for.

Grants

Grants are another form of free financial aid that do not need to
be repaid. Grants are funded by schools, private organizations, or
federal assistance programs. They are based on financial need, the
cost of the education program, and the student's part-time or
full-time status in the program.

Work-Study Programs

Work-study programs allow students to work part time while
attending school. These may be on-campus or off-campus jobs that
provide income to students to help pay for college costs.

— APPLY WHAT YOU'VE LEARNED —

Paying Off Student Loans

The first payment on a student loan is due, generally, six to nine months after you graduate. The normal repayment plan takes about ten years on average, unless you have a large amount of student loans which can take up to thirty years. So, you go to school for four to seven years, depending on what you study, and then repay the money for ten to thirty years! That doesn't make any sense.

DIRECTIONS: Using the figures provided, complete the calculations listed.

Here is what a typical student loan repayment might look like:

» **Loan Amount:** $27,000   » **Pay-Off Term:** 10 years

» **Interest Rate:** 5%   » **Monthly Payment:** $286

CALCULATE THE FOLLOWING

1. What is the total amount you would pay on your student loan after ten years of payments?

    ($286 per month payment for 120 months) $ _____

2. What is the difference between the original loan amount and the amount paid?

    $ _____

    What is your reaction to that figure?

    _____

    _____

    _____

- -

FINAL THOUGHT: The blessing of the LORD makes one rich, and He adds no sorrow with it.

PROVERBS 10:22 NKJV

Recap & Review

WHAT CAN YOU DO NOW?

 It's time to check your learning! Go back to the "I Can" statements at the beginning of this chapter. Place a check mark next to each statement that you can do now.

ILLUSTRATION TIME

Draw a picture representation of the following terms.

Scholarship

Debt

MONEY IN REVIEW

Circle the correct answer.

1. **The FICO score measures all of the following except:**
   - Ⓐ Debt history
   - Ⓑ Types of debt
   - Ⓒ New debt
   - Ⓓ Savings account balance

2. **Which of the following describes the best way to buy a car?**
   - Ⓐ Save up and pay cash for a used car in your price range
   - Ⓑ Ask to borrow money from your parents for the purchase
   - Ⓒ Save up a nice down payment and finance the rest
   - Ⓓ Allow your grandparents to cosign your loan for a new car

3. **The Federal Fair Debt Collection Practices Act of 1977 dictates:**
   - Ⓐ How much debt a person is allowed to carry
   - Ⓑ How debt collectors can interact with individuals
   - Ⓒ How much interest a lender can charge
   - Ⓓ How much of a debt a person must repay

4. **A fee that a bank, credit card, or other lender charges for the opportunity to purchase something and pay for it over time.**
   - Ⓐ Dividend
   - Ⓑ Credit
   - Ⓒ Interest
   - Ⓓ Finance rate

5. **Debt is marketed just like any other product.**
   - Ⓐ True
   - Ⓑ False

6. **You need to get a credit card or a car loan to build up your credit score.**
   - Ⓐ True
   - Ⓑ False

Your
dream job
can become a
reality
if you
start planning
now.

03

Education, Careers & Entrepreneurship

Set a course for your future.

43% of teens believe one day they will hold their dream job.[1]

71% of teens said they would choose to make more money over having their dream job.[2]

> Education is the key to unlock the golden door of freedom.

GEORGE WASHINGTON CARVER, scientist and inventor

> Far and away the best prize that life has to offer is the chance to work hard at work worth doing.

THEODORE ROOSEVELT, twenty-sixth president of the United States

> Hold on to instruction, do not let it go; guard it well, for it is your life.

PROVERBS 4:13 NIV

I Can...

☑ At the end of this chapter, come back to this list and mark the things you understand and could explain to a friend.

LESSON 1

☐ Identify personal skills and interests related to career options.

☐ Estimate the cost of a college education.

☐ Explore different sources for information about various career options.

LESSON 2

☐ Explain how education and/or training can impact lifetime income.

☐ Understand various types of income.

☐ Describe the impact of taxes on take-home pay.

LESSON 3

☐ Explain what it means to be an entrepreneur.

☐ Describe a variety of things I could do now to earn money.

☐ Recognize profit as an incentive for starting a business.

💬 The direction in which education starts a man will determine his future in life.

PLATO, philosopher

Career: Your line of work

Compensation: The total amount an employee is paid along with any benefits the employee receives

Earned Income: Income produced by working at a job as an employee

Employee: A person who works for someone else in exchange for money

Entrepreneur: A person who organizes and runs a business—and assumes the risks associated with the business

Passive Income: Income earned from things you own such as houses, land, or other buildings as well as money earned from books, software, or music you have written

Portfolio Income: Income from investments, interest, and earnings, including the sale of an investment at a higher price than you paid for it

Profit: When income is greater than expenses

Salary: Payment for work, usually calculated in periods of a week or longer

Take-home Pay: The amount of money you get to take home after taxes and deductions

Tuition: The charge or fee for going to a school/college/university

Wages: Payment for work, usually calculated in periods of an hour

Withholding: A portion of an employee's wages deducted for taxes

What Are You Going to Do?

With a plan, your dream job can become a reality.

YOUR SKILLS AND INTERESTS

We all have things we are good at and things we love to do. Those things might even turn into something you do for work or a **career**. Keep in mind that what you do for work may end up changing along the way. You may even work some jobs that you don't enjoy as you try to figure out what you really enjoy doing.

> Find a job or **a career** that blends two things: something you're _____ at and something you _____ to do.
>
> You will find satisfaction in your work if it is something you _____ and find _____ in.

You don't have to wait until you're an adult to start doing work you love. Jobs you do today—like babysitting, mowing yards, or making jewelry—will prepare you for a great career later on. Plus, you will learn some great life skills like how to work hard, get along with others, be honest, and stick with something even if it is hard.

 What kind of job would you consider your dream job?

_____

Top Jobs

Take a look at some of the top jobs:[3]

Best Health Care Jobs

Dentist

Nurse Practitioner

Physician

Dental Hygienist

Physical Therapist

Best Social Services Jobs

School Psychologist

Speech-Language Pathologist

Elementary School Teacher

High School Teacher

Middle School Teacher

Best Technology Jobs

Software Developer

Computer Systems Analyst

Information Security Analyst

Web Developer

Mechanical Engineer

Best Science/Math Jobs

Mathematician

Statistician

Audiologist

Civil Engineer

Epidemiologist

Best Business Jobs

Market Research Analyst

Marketing Manager

Accountant

Operations Research Analyst

Financial Advisor

Other Top Careers

Actor/Actress

Model

Professional Athlete

Singer/Songwriter

Author

JOBS 101

There are lots of different jobs. But just because a job pays well doesn't mean it will be something you enjoy. No matter how much you might make as a surgeon, if you faint at the sight of blood, medicine is probably not your best career path.

You may not have any idea right now what you want to do for a job or career. That's okay. If there is a job that seems interesting to you, spend some time researching the job. Here are some ideas to help get you started:

Find someone who is doing the job you think you want to do and _____ _____ about it.

A great place to find information on jobs is the

_____.

Also, look for information about:

» How much the job pays on average.

» How many years of school are typically required.

» What a career path looks like.

» Opportunities for job shadowing and internships—these can help you find out if you enjoy a job.

THE COST OF EDUCATION

Going to college can be expensive, but your options include two-year and four-year education plans at community colleges, private colleges, state colleges, and out-of-state colleges. You might also consider certifications, trade school, or on-the-job training. And don't forget to factor in the cost of books and other items.

JOURNAL QUESTION

What are two or three jobs that sound interesting to you? What makes them seem interesting?

_____

_____

_____

_____

Educational Choices

College Tuition Price Tags*

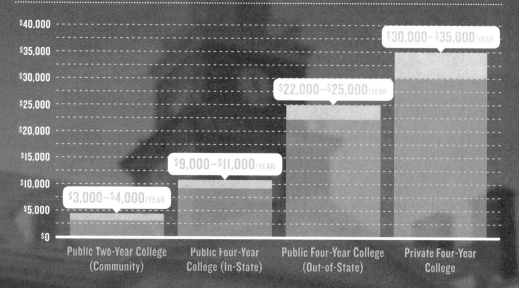

$40,000	
$35,000	$30,000–$35,000/YEAR
$30,000	
$25,000	$22,000–$25,000/YEAR
$20,000	
$15,000	
$10,000	$9,000–$11,000/YEAR
$5,000	$3,000–$4,000/YEAR
$0	

Public Two-Year College (Community) — Public Four-Year College (In-State) — Public Four-Year College (Out-of-State) — Private Four-Year College

Other College Expenses*

$5,000–$15,000 PER YEAR	$700–$2,500 PER YEAR	$1,000–$3,000 PER YEAR
Housing and meals	Books and supplies	Other expenses (transportation and personal)

Cutting College Costs

» Go to a community college and live at home for the first year or two.

» Buy used textbooks rather than new when possible.

» Choose the right meal plan.

» Look for scholarships and grants.

» Pick up a part-time job.

» Take dual enrollment/A.P. (advanced placement) classes in high school to earn early credits (cheaper than tuition).

*Note: these costs are averages at the time of this writing

The Perfect Job

Finding work that matters is a big deal. A lot of people feel trapped in a career because they chose a job for the wrong reasons or stayed with a job just to pay bills. The key is to find something you are good at and love to do.

DIRECTIONS: Take some time to consider your responses to the following questions. Then use your answers to begin thinking about possible jobs you would enjoy.

What are some of your interests?

_____

_____

_____

What are some of your hobbies?

_____

_____

_____

What activities do you really enjoy doing?

_____

_____

_____

What would you consider the perfect job? Why?

_____

_____

_____

What are your favorite subjects in school?

_____

_____

_____

What kinds of things are you really good at?

_____

_____

_____

FINAL THOUGHT: All hard work brings a profit, but mere talk leads only to poverty.

PROVERBS 14:23 NIV

Earning an Income

Good grades now will help you make more money later.

EDUCATION AND INCOME

Part of growing up is finding a career and making some money. Everyone wants to make big money right out of high school. Most jobs, however, have a "starting salary"—what you will make when you first start. Don't be unrealistic about how much money you might make.

Will you make more money if you get a college degree? Most studies indicate that you will. Also, those with a degree are more likely to find a job or be hired ahead of someone without one. How much more money can you make? It really depends on the job.[4]

> ## Research indicates it could be anywhere from
>
> _____ — _____ more per year.

That means that over a thirty-year period of working in a career, you could make an extra $450,000–$900,000!

Many careers require at least a four-year college degree. Before you pursue a particular field of study, however, do some research into how much you might expect to earn. Then balance that with the cost of your education. For example, if you think you want to become an athletic trainer and the average starting **salary** is $35,000–40,000 per year, it doesn't make a lot of sense to go to a big-name or out-of-state college for four years and pay over $100,000 in **tuition**.

> ## Just having a college _____ doesn't guarantee you a job.

What is the most money you have made in one day?

EMPLOYEE BENEFITS

> A compensation package is made up of what you will get _____ and your _____.
>
> ₁₀   ₁₁

When you work as an **employee**, what you get paid is called your **wages**. The benefits in your **compensation** package are extra perks. These might include health insurance, dental insurance, and life insurance, but they can also include investment options, days off when you're sick, and even paid time off for vacations.

> The money you get to take home and see in your bank account is called your _____ pay.
>
> ₁₂

When you work, you expect to get paid. Here is a quick look at three basic types of income, including your paycheck. Keep in mind you will pay taxes on all of these:

» **Earned Income:** Any income (wages/salary) produced by working at a job as an employee.

» **Portfolio Income:** Income from investments, interest, and earnings including the sale of investments at a higher price than you paid for them.

» **Passive Income:** Income earned from things you own such as houses, land, or other buildings as well as money earned from books, software, or music you have written or produced.

PAYCHECK DEDUCTIONS

One of the fantastic parts of having a job is getting paid. When you work for an employer, however, you will have a variety of taxes taken out of your pay. This is called **withholding** because your employer withholds, or holds back, a portion of your pay for tax purposes as required by the government. These deductions impact your **take-home pay**, which is the actual amount of money you get to keep and spend. So, you will take home less that what you really earn.

TAXES

First, there is federal income tax that goes to the federal government for their programs and budget. Then there is often a state income tax that goes to your state government for their programs and budget. You will see deductions for Social Security and Medicare. Social Security provides benefits for retired workers. Medicare is a program to help with medical expenses after you turn sixty-five. The deductions are 12.4% for Social Security and 2.9% for Medicare. Your employer pays half of the total Social Security (6.2%) and Medicare (1.45%) deductions, and you pay the other half. If you are self-employed, you have to pay the full amount.

INSURANCE

If you pay for health insurance, dental or vision insurances, life insurance, or any other benefits at your place of employment, you will also see those deductions reflected on your paycheck. After all of the taxes, insurances, and benefits are taken out, what's left is considered your take-home pay—what you get to take home and spend.

JOURNAL QUESTION

What are some of the things that you would like to do in the future? How can your education help you do those things?

There may be people who have more talent than you, but there's no excuse for anyone to work harder than you do.

DEREK JETER, Major League Baseball World Series Champion

— APPLY WHAT YOU'VE LEARNED —

Your Take-Home Pay

Imagine you plan to work twenty hours per week and you find a job that pays $10 per hour. That means your paycheck will be $200 each week, right? Wrong.

DIRECTIONS: Use the figures provided to calculate how much money will be deducted from your paycheck and how much money you will have to spend.

WIDGET CO.
1921 Business Way
Anytown TN, 37027

CHECK STUB FOR 3/24–3/31

YOUR NAME
3150 Ridgeview Drive, Apt. 214
Anytown TN, 37027

EMPLOYEE ID# 0557498 // DEPT.# 0032

RATE	CURRENT $	YEAR-TO-DATE $	TAX		CURRENT $	YEAR-TO-DATE $
$10 / HR	$200	1,600.00	FITWH	A	20.00	160.00
			SOC	B	12.40	99.20
			MED	C	2.90	23.20
			SITWH	D	10.00	80.00

Your employer will withhold the following taxes from your $200 paycheck:

A **Federal Income Tax (10%):** $20.00 **C** **Medicare Tax (1.45%):** $2.90

B **Social Security Tax (6.2%):** $12.40 **D** **State Income Tax (5%):** $10.00

CALCULATE THE FOLLOWING

1. How much money in taxes will be withheld from your pay each week:

   $ _____

2. After all of the taxes are withheld from your $200 paycheck, how much money will you actually take home each week (your take-home pay)?

   $ _____

- -

FINAL THOUGHT: A man's heart plans his way, but the LORD directs his steps.

PROVERBS 16:9 NKJV

Be Your Own Boss

Starting your own business is something you can do now.

YOUR OWN BUSINESS

An entrepreneur is someone who _____ and _____ his or her own business.

In the US, there are more than 28 million small businesses. These are defined as having fewer than five hundred employees. More than 50% of workers in the US work in a small business. And more than 75% are self-employed, running their own businesses.[5] Earning a profit is one incentive that leads many people to start their own companies. **Entrepreneurs** often take risks that are associated with creating and producing new goods or starting a new business.

The first thing to do is to figure out a business idea that will make _____.

YOU COULD BE AN ENTREPRENEUR

_____% of high school and middle school students plan to start their own businesses some day.

What is really cool is that of those students, 38% will invent something that changes the world in some way. And 3% of teens have already started their own businesses.[6]

YOU COULD BE AN ENTREPRENEUR (CONTINUED)

Three of the most famous entrepreneurs are Steve Jobs (Apple), Mark Zuckerberg (Facebook), and Bill Gates (Microsoft). The businesses they started at young ages and the products they created impact most of our lives on an everyday basis.

So, what qualities does it take to be an entrepreneur? Some common qualities include creativity, the ability to lead, passion for your idea or work, flexibility, attention to detail, and a strong belief in yourself.

WHAT CAN YOU DO?

Yes, you can make money by starting your own business—even as a middle schooler. The following list will help you think about potential businesses you could start. Circle any ideas that catch your attention or write some of your own ideas.

- » Pet sitting/walking
- » Handmade greeting cards
- » Home-baked cookies/cupcakes
- » Cake pops
- » Car washing
- » Web site design

- » Blogging
- » Jewelry design
- » Clothing design
- » Collecting recyclables
- » Lawn mowing
- » Kids party clown/ juggler/entertainer

- » Candy bar sales
- » Fresh-baked pet treats
- » Online selling (such as Etsy)
- » Other: _____
- » Other: _____
- » Other: _____

WANT TO LEARN MORE? Go to www.foundationsU.com/middle-school **to learn more about the teen entrepreneurs featured in the video for this lesson.**

JOURNAL QUESTION

If you were to start your own business, what would it be? Why would you choose that?

_____

_____

_____

Batteries Included

Nobody likes getting an electronic gadget or device without the batteries needed to make it work! A battery is a source of energy. Some things come with batteries and some don't.

The battery metaphor can also be applied to people. Michael Hyatt, a writer and speaker on the topic of leadership development, describes two types of employees: those who have their own energy source and those who depend on others for energy.

Employees *without* batteries drain the energy out of the others around them. Nobody wants to work with those types of people.

Six *Batteries-Included* Ways to Get a Job

1 Don't create drama.

2 Don't gossip or backbite.

3 Be positive and encouraging.

4 Be a self-starter.

5 Accept responsibility.

6 Show up on time.

The Cost of Business

There are always costs associated with business, including the cost of your time. If you sell baked goods or make jewelry, you have to buy your supplies. If you mow yards, you have to pay for gas, trimmer line, and maintenance. One of the most important aspects of running a business is managing your income and expenses. A basic business tool is a profit and loss statement (a P&L) that helps you track all of your income and expenses so you can see how profitable your business is.

DIRECTIONS: Using the information provided, calculate how much Jason and Brandi made or lost during a four-week period. Then determine which business was more profitable.

I. Jason's Yard Work

Jason uses six gallons of gasoline ($2.50 per gallon) every four weeks. Jason charges $20 per yard including trimming and $15 without trimming. He mows three yards each week that require trimming and one yard that does not require trimming. So, Jason earns $75 per week. He had to buy a new spool of trimmer line this month ($10 total) as well as a new spark plug ($4) and air filter for his mower ($15). During the last week of the month, Jason picked up one new customer for both mowing and trimming.

INCOME		EXPENSES	
$75 per week (×4 weeks)	$ _____	6 gallons gas ($2.50 per gallon)	$ 15
Extra yard (trim and mow)	$ _____	Spool of trimmer line	$ _____
		Spark plug for mower	$ _____
		Air filter for mower	$ _____
TOTAL INCOME	$ _____	**TOTAL EXPENSES**	$ _____

TOTAL PROFIT (OR LOSS) $ _____

2. Brandi's Bangles

Brandi loves to make and sell jewelry. This month, Brandi bought these supplies for her business: ten packs of colored beads ($3 each), five packs of crystal beads ($4 each), five packs of decorative glass beads ($5 each), and six decorative charms ($5 each). She also purchased two spools of silver beading wire ($7.50 each), two packs of necklace clasps ($5 each), and two packs of earring wires ($5 each). Brandi sells basic necklaces for $10 each and basic earrings for $5 for a set of two. She sells fancy necklaces for $20 each and the matching earrings for $10 for a set of two. Over four weeks, Brandi sold a total of seven basic necklaces, four sets of basic earrings, six fancy necklaces, and four sets of fancy earrings.

INCOME		EXPENSES	
7 basic necklaces ($10 each)	$ _____	10 packs colored beads ($3 each)	$ 30
4 sets basic earrings ($5 each)	$ _____	5 packs crystal beads ($4 each)	$ _____
6 fancy necklaces ($20 each)	$ _____	5 packs glass beads ($5 each)	$ _____
4 sets fancy earrings ($10 each)	$ _____	6 decorative charms ($5 each)	$ _____
		2 spools silver wire ($7.50 each)	$ _____
		2 packs necklace clasps ($5 each)	$ _____
		2 packs earring wires ($5 each)	$ _____
TOTAL INCOME $ _____		**TOTAL EXPENSES** $ _____	

TOTAL PROFIT (OR LOSS) $ _____

3. Whose Business is More Profitable?   ☐ JASON'S   ☐ BRANDI'S

- -

FINAL THOUGHT: Whatever you do, do it enthusiastically.

COLOSSIANS 3:23 HCSB

Recap & Review

WHAT CAN YOU DO NOW?

 It's time to check your learning! Go back to the "I Can" statements at the beginning of this chapter. Place a check mark next to each statement that you can do now.

ILLUSTRATION TIME

Draw a picture representation of the following terms.

Entrepreneur

Profit

SELF TEST

Circle the correct answer.

1. When choosing a career, find something that
- **A** Makes you a lot of money
- **B** You are good at and you love to do
- **C** All your friends enjoy
- **D** Will be completely boring

2. Non-wage compensation provided by your employer are called
- **A** Withholdings
- **B** Take-home pay
- **C** Income
- **D** Employee benefits

3. The amount of money you get in your paycheck after taxes are taken out is called
- **A** Withholdings
- **B** Benefit pay
- **C** Take-home pay
- **D** Gross income

4. Money which is taken out for taxes is called
- **A** Withholding
- **B** Employee benefits
- **C** Take-home pay
- **D** Net pay

5. Someone who starts and runs his or her own business is called a(n)
- **A** Creditor
- **B** Employee
- **C** Manager
- **D** Entrepreneur

6. Which are the correct amounts withheld for Social Security and Medicare taxes from a person's paycheck?
- **A** Social Security Tax (8.2%), Medicare Tax (2.45%)
- **B** Social Security Tax (6.2%), Medicare Tax (1.45%)
- **C** Social Security Tax (10.2%), Medicare Tax (4.45%)
- **D** Social Security Tax (3.2%), Medicare Tax (3.45%)

Insurance is like a shield to protect you.

04

Investing, Insurance & Identity Theft

Prepare for the worst; plan for the best.

50% of people believe they do not have enough insurance coverage.[1]

59% of teens believe they will do better financially than their parents.[2]

> Money is like manure: Left in one pile, it stinks. Spread around, it makes things grow.

DAVE RAMSEY

> Money is good for nothing unless you know the value of it by experience.

P.T. BARNUM, showman and businessman

> A good person leaves an inheritance for their children's children.

PROVERBS 13:22 NIV

I Can...

At the end of this chapter, come back to this list and mark the things you understand and could explain to a friend.

LESSON 1

☐ Explain the difference between saving and investing.

☐ Describe the impact of inflation.

☐ Understand the time value of money.

LESSON 2

☐ Recognize how investing can help me build wealth.

☐ Compare the various types of investments.

☐ Explain the power of compound interest.

LESSON 3

☐ Explain the purpose of insurance.

☐ Analyze different types of insurance.

☐ Recognize the difference between an insurance premium and an insurance deductible.

LESSON 4

☐ Understand the issue of identity theft.

☐ Describe problems that occur as a result of identity theft.

☐ List ways to protect myself from identity theft.

Bonds: A loan of money to a business or government that is paid back with interest over time

CD: Certificate of Deposit; saving certificate with a fixed saving period and fixed interest rate

Deductible: Amount you must pay before you receive any benefits from your insurance coverage

Fraud: Wrongful or criminal deception for financial gain

Identity Theft: The illegal use of someone's personal information to purchase items or receive benefits

Inflation: The rate at which the prices for goods and services rise

Insurance: An agreement in which a policyholder transfers the risk for potential financial losses to another party in exchange for a fee

Investment Advisor: A financial professional who manages investments and has been trained and licensed to do so

Liability Insurance: A policy that protects an individual in the event of a lawsuit due to injury as the result of an accident

Mutual Fund: A collection of stocks, bonds, and other investments owned by a group of investors who put their money together

Premium: Amount that is paid monthly, quarterly, semi-annually, or annually to purchase insurance coverage

Stocks: Investments that represent small pieces of ownership in a company

Time Value of Money: The potential impact of inflation and interest on money

Investing for the Long Term

Saving is for the short term; investing is long term.

LESSON 1

SAVING VS. INVESTING

When it comes to handling your money, there are two important words you need to know: *saving* and *investing*. If your goal is to keep your money safe and have it when you need it, savings is the way to go.

Saving is for the _____ _____.

When you put money into a savings account, it will gain a small amount of interest. It won't grow a lot, but it will grow some. When you save, you are putting your money somewhere for less than five years. This is money you want to be liquid, meaning you are able to get to it quickly when you need it. This money is generally kept safe at a local bank in a savings or money market account.

Investing is for the _____ _____.

If your goal is to build wealth—and you are willing to leave your money alone for five years or more—you could see a mathematical explosion (compound interest) happen when you invest. Remember, compound interest helps your investment gain money. But, you also have the risk of losing some money. Typically, your money will grow and make more money for you when it is invested. For example, a deposit of $1,000 into a .005% interest rate savings account would only earn $25 after five years (and only $50 at 1%). You aren't making a lot of money, but you aren't losing any either. However, if you invested that same amount with an annual 10% interest rate compounded monthly, you would end up with $1,645 after five years. But, you could also lose money, so there is some risk involved.

 Would you rather have $1 million right now or a penny doubled every day for a month?

THE VALUE OF MONEY

The **time value of money** means that money today is always worth more than money later. That is a basic concept in personal finance. Yes, it sounds weird. Isn't a $100 bill today worth the same as a $100 bill next year? Technically, yes. But will that $100 buy the same amount of stuff next year as it will today? Probably not, because things will cost more. The time value of money includes a loss of value due to **inflation** (the increase in price of stuff over time).

> ## Because of inflation, your money can be worth _____ in the future.

Here's an example of the impact of inflation at an annual 3% rate. Your $100 will only buy $97 worth of stuff next year and then only $94 the next. But, in twenty years, that same $100 would only buy about $40 worth of stuff.

> ## When you invest your money, it can be worth _____ in the future.

The time value of money also means your money can be worth more when you invest it and gain compound interest. Long-term money goals are for things five years or more into the future. One of those goals could be planning for retirement. That is when investing and the power of compound interest come into play. Many students like to dream about being millionaires, but they think it will never happen. However, retiring a millionaire is a great example of a long-term goal. The good news is that you can retire a millionaire if you will begin investing early.

JOURNAL QUESTION

How have you seen the impact of inflation on the things you buy?

_____

_____

_____

_____

— APPLY WHAT YOU'VE LEARNED —

The Impact of Inflation

These charts show the change in prices of four common items, based on national averages, from the 1970s until now. Prices go up each year due to inflation.

DIRECTIONS: Research the current pricing for each of the graphs below. Write down today's price in the blank provided and plot its location on the graph.

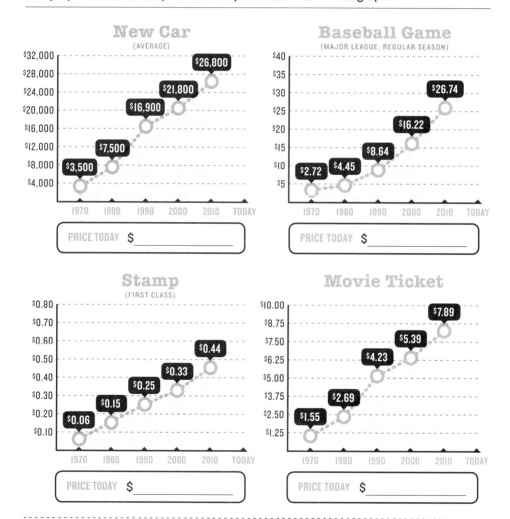

New Car
(AVERAGE)

$32,000 — $26,800
$28,000
$24,000 — $21,800
$20,000
$16,000 — $16,900
$12,000
$8,000 — $7,500
$4,000 — $3,500

1970   1980   1990   2000   2010   TODAY

PRICE TODAY $ _____

Baseball Game
(MAJOR LEAGUE, REGULAR SEASON)

$40 — $26.74
$35
$30
$25
$20 — $16.22
$15
$10 — $8.64
$5 — $2.72 $4.45

1970   1980   1990   2000   2010   TODAY

PRICE TODAY $ _____

Stamp
(FIRST CLASS)

$0.80 — $0.44
$0.70
$0.60
$0.50
$0.40 — $0.33
$0.30 — $0.25
$0.20 — $0.15
$0.10 — $0.06

1970   1980   1990   2000   2010   TODAY

PRICE TODAY $ _____

Movie Ticket

$10.00 — $7.89
$8.75
$7.50 — $5.39
$6.25 — $4.23
$5.00
$3.75 — $2.69
$2.50 — $1.55
$1.25

1970   1980   1990   2000   2010   TODAY

PRICE TODAY $ _____

FINAL THOUGHT: Wise people think before they act; fools don't.

PROVERBS 13:16 NLT

Watching Money Grow

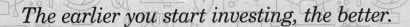

The earlier you start investing, the better.

WHAT IS "THE MARKET"?

Maybe you have heard of the stock market but you have no idea what it is or how it works. That's okay. Many people have a hard time understanding it. The stock market is just one example of a financial market—places where people are able to invest their money.

Maybe this will help. Think of the stock market like a supermarket where lots of different things are bought and sold. Some people want to buy yogurt, some want to buy carrots, and others want to buy candy. There are a lot of different name brands as well as generic versions of different products. And everything has a different price. This is the same for financial markets. There are a lot of different things you can "buy." And you can choose what you want to invest in.

RIDING THE ROLLER COASTER

To help you better understand financial markets, think of a roller coaster. Why? Because if you look at a picture of the gains and losses in the stock market over time, it really does look like a roller coaster. There are lots of ups and downs. In the stock market, the parts that go up are places where investments are making money. The parts that go down, on the other hand, indicate places where investments are losing money. However, the likelihood that you will make money over the long term is pretty good. In fact, 100% of the twenty-year periods in the stock market since 1950 have made money.[3] But, just like being on a roller coaster, you will get hurt if you jump off before the ride is over.

 What would you do if you were a millionaire? Why?

WATCHING YOUR MONEY GROW

Investing simply means putting your money in something that will make a profit for you. There are a lot of different types of investments, so it is helpful to understand a little about each one.

Some investments have very low risk but you won't make a lot of money. Other investments have more risk of losing money, but you also have the potential to earn more money.

The reason to invest is to make more _____ for something like planning for retirement.

_____ represent ownership in a company.

_____ _____ are investments owned by a group of investors.

INVESTING 101

Long-term investing is investing for _____ years or more.

When you're ready to invest, it's always a good idea to get help from a professional **investment advisor**. While you may not understand anything about bonds, the stock market, mutual funds, or investments, an investment advisor can help you. It is always important to understand the things you invest in. Here is a quick look at the basics of some of the most common investments available:

MONEY MARKET ACCOUNTS

Money market accounts pay only a little more than a regular savings account, so you won't make a bunch of money off interest in them. However, these are low-risk investments and are a great place to park your emergency fund.

CDS (CERTIFICATES OF DEPOSIT)

CDs are another type of a low-risk savings option where you agree to leave your money alone for a period of time (such as six months, one year, or more). In exchange for leaving it alone, you will earn a higher interest rate.

BONDS

Bonds are basically a loan of money, like an I.O.U., to a corporation or government agency that needs to finance a project or an activity. The borrower agrees to pay the loan back (with interest) after a certain period of time. Bonds carry more risk than basic bank accounts so you could lose some money.

STOCKS

Unlike bonds, **stocks** are not a loan of money, but they actually represent ownership. You buy (invest in) a piece of the company. You make money as the company grows and makes more money. Since you own a share, that means you get a portion of the profit. Single stocks, however, carry a high degree of risk. While you might make money, you could also lose a lot of money.

MUTUAL FUNDS

Mutual funds are investments owned by a group of people who put their money together to mutually fund an investment. That's where the name comes from—a mutually funded investment, also known as a mutual fund. The money is used to invest in a collection of stocks, bonds, or other investments. Mutual funds are good long-term investments. Spreading your investments across a variety of mutual funds is called diversification and that helps lower your risk of losing money.

JOURNAL QUESTION

How can long-term investing help you become a millionaire?

_____

_____

_____

_____

Growing Money

You've probably heard the phrase "If money grew on trees." That would be pretty cool, right? Whenever you want to buy something, you could just go to the backyard and pull a couple of $20 bills off the tree. Sadly, money doesn't grow on trees. But if you will invest money and leave it alone for a long time, say forty years, you will see some incredible growth. Compound interest becomes a mathematical explosion for your investments. For example, take a look at what would happen if you invested $150 per month with 10% interest compounded monthly:

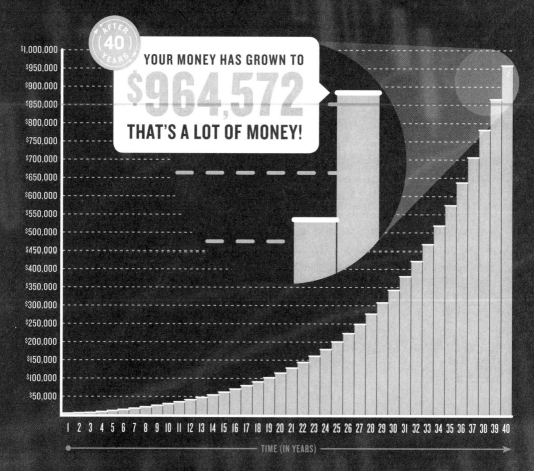

AFTER **40** YEARS

YOUR MONEY HAS GROWN TO

$964,572

THAT'S A LOT OF MONEY!

TIME (IN YEARS)

— APPLY WHAT YOU'VE LEARNED —

Interest Expanded

In Chapter 1, Lesson 2, you learned about the power of compound interest. Remember, it is a mathematical explosion that happens to your money. If you made a one-time investment of $1,000 at 10% interest compounded monthly, after just five years, the $1,000 investment would grow to $1,645.

If you were to leave the money alone, with monthly compounded interest the investment would continue to grow and begin to look like this:

10 years = $2,707 | 15 years = $4,454 | 20 years = $7,328 | 25 years = $12,057

THE FORMULA FOR COMPOUND INTEREST: **FV** is the future value with compound interest, **PV** is the present value based on the principal amount, **r** is the interest rate expressed as a decimal, **m** is the number of times per year the interest is compounded (monthly/annually), and **t** is the number of years/periods you leave the money invested.

$$FV = PV(1 + r/m)^{mt}$$

For example, here is what the calculation looks like for the 20-year figure:

$$FV = 1,000(1 + .10/12)^{12 \times 20} = 7328.0736$$

DIRECTIONS: Using the formula for compound interest, calculate how much this $1,000 investment could grow to after thirty and forty years with 10% interest compounded monthly?

1. What would the total be after 30 years?

   $ _____

2. What would the total be after 40 years?

   $ _____

- -

FINAL THOUGHT: Dishonest money dwindles away, but whoever gathers money little by little makes it grow.

PROVERBS 13:11 NIV

Protect Yourself

Insurance is an important part of a financial plan.

WHAT IS INSURANCE?

If you've ever played a survival-based game, one of the first things you need to do is build, create, or buy some way to protect yourself. You need a shelter and usually some sort of armor. Sure, you want to start exploring, but you will last longer in the game if you take care of this basic protection first.

_____ is the equivalent of building your shelter or fortress in a game.

Insurance is a vital part of a good financial plan. The right types of insurance act as protective barriers between your money (and investments) and life events. Without insurance, you are one accident away from losing everything.

What are some insurance companies you have heard about?

_____

HOW DOES INSURANCE WORK?

The money you pay for insurance is called a _____.

A **premium** is the monthly, quarterly, or annual cost for your insurance coverage. When you pay your premium, you are paying the insurance company to take on any financial risk in the event of an accident and to pay for some of the costs.

For example, your parents probably pay for health insurance. So, if you get hurt, go to the hospital, and need surgery with an overnight stay, it won't cost your parents a fortune to take care of you. The insurance company would pay for some of the doctor and hospital charges because your parents pay the monthly insurance premium. However, your parents would probably still have to pay something—their **deductible**—but they wouldn't have to pay for everything. Without health insurance, your parents could be facing thousands and thousands of dollars' worth of medical bills.

A _____ is the part you pay before the insurance company pays their part.

INSURANCE IS IMPORTANT

You can buy different types of insurance from an insurance agent or broker— someone who is trained and licensed to sell insurance. They will be able to help you find the best insurance options at the best prices. Your employer may also offer several types of insurance for you, and they may even pay for part or all of it.

When you start buying insurances, make sure your home and auto policies have enough **liability insurance**. Liability insurance protects you if someone were hurt on your property or as a result of an automobile accident involving your car. It doesn't cost very much, and it is really important to have in place.

JOURNAL QUESTION

Write down two things you learned about insurance.

_____

_____

_____

_____

Types of Insurance

There are a lot of different types of insurance that you can purchase—some are really good ideas and some are really bad ideas. So, when it comes time for you to get insurance, what should you get? Here are seven basic types of insurance that everyone should have:

 **1 Homeowners or Renters Insurance:** protects your stuff where you live.

 **2 Auto Insurance:** protects your car, the people in your car, and you.

3 Health Insurance: protects you when you are sick or hurt and need medical care.

 4 Disability Insurance: protects you if an injury prevents you from doing your job and earning an income.

 5 Long-term Care Insurance: provides your health care needs at age sixty or older.

 6 Identity Theft Protection: protects you from fraud.

 7 Life Insurance: protects and provides for family members in the event of death.

— APPLY WHAT YOU'VE LEARNED —

Got You Covered

Nobody likes paying for insurance. But, insurance is very important to have. Insurance protects you, and your money, when something unexpected happens.

DIRECTIONS: Using the information you learned in this lesson, match the type of insurance that would cover each situation.

A Homeowners/Renters Insurance

B Auto Insurance

C Health Insurance

D Disability Insurance

E Long-term Care Insurance

F Identity Theft Insurance

G Life Insurance

---

1. _____ You are involved in a traffic accident on the way to school. Nobody was hurt, but your mom's car is messed up beyond repair.

2. _____ Your uncle expresses concern about how your aunt will pay the bills in the event of his death.

3. _____ Due to poor health, your grandmother had to move into a nursing home.

4. _____ You tried to score the winning goal but broke your leg during the play. You are on your way to the hospital.

5. _____ Your mom saw some charges in the bank statement that she did not make; she is afraid someone stole her debit card information.

6. _____ Your dad was hurt at work and the doctors say he won't be able to go back to work for at least nine months, maybe even a year.

7. _____ Your home catches on fire. The firefighters put it out and save most of your stuff. However, most of the furniture is destroyed and there are a lot of repairs needed to the house.

- -

FINAL THOUGHT: Do your planning and prepare your fields before building your house.

PROVERBS 24:27 NLT

A Case of Stolen Identity

Take responsibility to protect your money and identity.

IDENTITY THEFT: A BIG DEAL

You've probably seen the humorous ads on TV or even a movie showing someone using another person's credit card, debit card, or personal information to buy a bunch of stuff. But there is nothing funny about **identity theft**. In fact, it is called **fraud**! When you intentionally use someone's credit cards or other information to buy stuff for yourself, that is just wrong, and it is illegal.

> _____ _____ is when someone takes your personal information.

12

One out of every fourteen people (7%) has been the victim of fraud in the form of identity theft. Every seventy-nine seconds, a thief steals someone's identity. And about half of all identity theft cases are done by someone the victim knows.[4]

 What are some types of information you should never share on social media?

STEALING YOUR INFO

Identity theft can leave you, the victim, with a bunch of problems. You could lose money if it is stolen from your accounts. Your credit can be destroyed by fraudulent charges. You could also end up with a huge variety of legal issues, and it can take a long time to correct the situation. Victims of identify theft also deal with emotional issues because their personal privacy has been invaded.

All a thief needs is some of your _____ information. [13]

Your name, address, Social Security number, and your birth date are all that someone needs to open fake accounts in your name. A stolen wallet or purse provides quick access to credit and debit cards. Also, personal information can be found on things in the mail or thrown in the trash. Computers, smartphones, and tablets also provide ways for thieves to get this information. Some of the greatest leaks of personal information, however, can be found on social media sites.

THE HIGH COST OF IDENTITY THEFT

You need to protect yourself from identity theft. When thieves steal your information and use it to buy stuff, the total dollar amount can really add up. With over 300 million people in the US, the total cost works out to about $1,500 per person![5]

Here is a way to think about that. Let's say you can purchase a new movie release online for $20. That means an identity thief could buy seventy-five online movies with your money. Or, the thief could buy fifteen new pairs of $100 athletic shoes. Or maybe twenty-five $60 video games.

And if you are a victim of identity theft, it can cost you a lot of time trying to fix the situation. The bottom line is that identity theft is a huge pain and often carries a high cost.

The most important thing to do—online and everywhere—is to stop and _____ _____ what you're doing. [14]

JOURNAL QUESTION

What are some things you should do to protect yourself against identity theft?

_____

_____

Protect Yourself from Identity Theft

Identity theft is a huge problem today. You need to take some practical steps to protect yourself.

Here are some things you can do to protect yourself from identity theft:

» Always protect your debit and credit card numbers.

» Be aware of people looking over your shoulder at personal info.

» Don't carry your Social Security card in your wallet or purse.

» Use strong passwords, keep them in a safe place, and change them often.

» Be careful what you post on social media. For example: Don't post that you will be out of town for a week or two.

» Don't post the exact date and place of your birth.

» Don't share passwords or PIN numbers with others.

» Don't give away personal identity details.

» Never open or answer emails if you don't know who sent them.

» Shred or destroy mail containing personal information.

» Don't use the same password for all of your accounts.

 Never post your exact date and place of birth. It's invaluable information to identity thieves.

JOHN SILEO, identity-theft expert, author

Identity Theft

DIRECTIONS: Decide if the following statements are true or false based on what you have learned.

1. Your greatest risk of identity theft is typically between ages 18 and 24.

   ☐ TRUE   ☐ FALSE

2. There is nothing wrong with letting your best friend use your debit card and your PIN number.

   ☐ TRUE   ☐ FALSE

3. 7% of people will become victims of identity theft.

   ☐ TRUE   ☐ FALSE

4. The average cost of identity theft works out to $1,500 per person.

   ☐ TRUE   ☐ FALSE

5. There is no problem posting your birth date and cell phone number on social media sites.

   ☐ TRUE   ☐ FALSE

6. Identity theft is considered fraud—and that is illegal.

   ☐ TRUE   ☐ FALSE

7. All an identity thief needs is your name, address, Social Security number, and birth date to open accounts in your name.

   ☐ TRUE   ☐ FALSE

8. Identity theft is pretty rare, so you don't have to worry about it.

   ☐ TRUE   ☐ FALSE

9. Identity theft is not a big deal because it is easy to fix.

   ☐ TRUE   ☐ FALSE

10. Half of all identity theft is committed by someone the victim knows personally (for example, a family member).

   ☐ TRUE   ☐ FALSE

FINAL THOUGHT: Treasures gained by wickedness do not profit.
PROVERBS 10:2 ESV

Recap & Review

 It's time to check your learning! Go back to the "I Can" statements at the beginning of this chapter. Place a check mark next to each statement that you can do now.

ILLUSTRATION TIME

Draw a picture representation of the following terms.

Insurance

Investment

SELF TEST

Circle the correct answer.

1. **True or False: Investing is for the long term, meaning more than five years.**

   Ⓐ True

   Ⓑ False

2. **Of the following, which one is the best place to keep your emergency fund?**

   Ⓐ Money market account

   Ⓑ Stocks

   Ⓒ Mutual funds

   Ⓓ Certificates of deposit

3. **This represents small pieces of ownership in a company.**

   Ⓐ Bonds

   Ⓑ Mutual funds

   Ⓒ Stocks

   Ⓓ Certificates of deposit

4. **A savings account should be used for your**

   Ⓐ Short-term savings goals

   Ⓑ Long-term savings goals

5. **The money you pay for an insurance policy is called your**

   Ⓐ Dividend

   Ⓑ Coverage

   Ⓒ Co-pay

   Ⓓ Premium

6. **Which of the following types of insurance would cover costs associated with the theft of belongings from your house?**

   Ⓐ Health

   Ⓑ Disability

   Ⓒ Homeowners/renters

   Ⓓ Long-term care

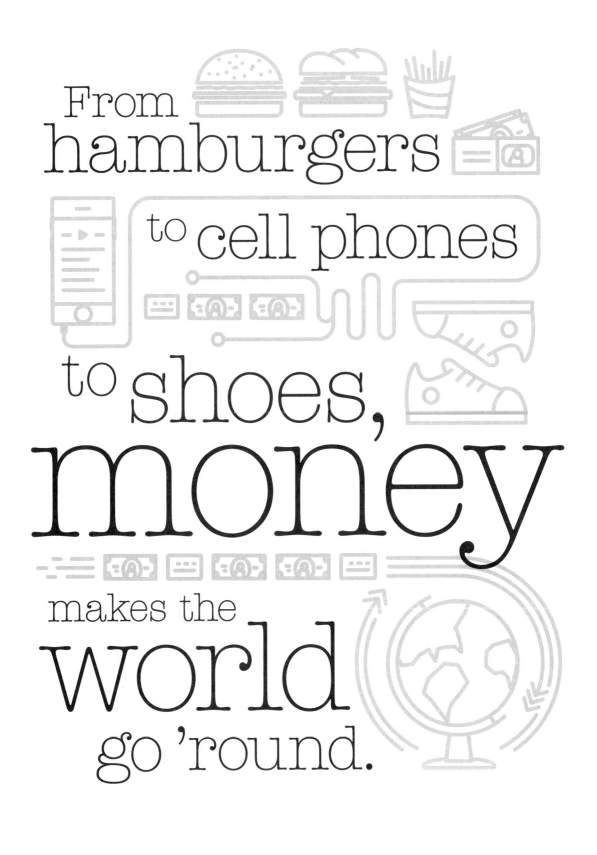

From hamburgers to cell phones to shoes, money makes the world go 'round.

05

Global Economics

How money moves around the world.

40% of vegetables and fruits in US stores are imported from other countries.[1]

38% of people in the world today survive on less than $2 per day.[2]

> Doing well is the result of doing good. That's what capitalism is all about.

RALPH WALDO EMERSON, writer and poet

> Facebook was not originally created to be a company. It was built to accomplish a social mission—to make the world more open and connected.

MARK ZUCKERBERG, creator of Facebook

> These were your merchants in choice items—in purple clothes, in embroidered garments, in chests of multicolored apparel, in sturdy woven cords, which were in your marketplace. The ships of Tarshish were carriers of your merchandise.

EZEKIEL 27:24-25 NKJV

I Can...

LESSON 1

☐ Compare and contrast different types of economic systems.

☐ Explain the movement of goods and services.

☐ Understand the concept of supply and demand.

LESSON 2

☐ Explain the chain of production process.

☐ Define gross domestic product (GDP).

☐ Describe the difference between developed countries and developing countries.

LESSON 3

☐ Define globalization.

☐ Explain how global trade works.

☐ Describe scarcity and rationing.

> The goal of every business is to make a profit. If they don't, they close.
>
> DAVE RAMSEY

Capital: Refers to money; specifically financial assets or the financial value of someone's assets

Capitalism: A system of economics based on the private ownership of business and the products (goods and services) made and sold

Chain of Production: The development and movement of goods and services through an economic system

Economics: The study of how a society manages all of its resources to produce and distribute goods and services

GDP / Gross Domestic Product: The total market value of all the goods and services produced by a country during a specified period

Globalization: The interaction between the various countries of the world

Interdependence: The dependence upon other countries resulting in the trade for goods and services

Rationing: A process to control the amount of goods and services being used; typically when there is scarcity

Scarcity: A condition of limited resources and unlimited wants by people

Socialism: An economic system based on public or collective (such as government) ownership of resources and production

Economic Systems

Supply and demand influences the cost of everything.

ECONOMICS 101

Global economics impacts all of us. You are probably wearing something right now that came from another country. The money we spend to buy products connects countries all over the world. And that money impacts the economy of countries all around the world.

When most people hear the word **economics**, they think about money. But economics is about more than just money. Trading goods, buying and selling, using resources, and monitoring cash flow are all ways we participate in economics on a daily basis.

_____ is the study of how a society manages all of its resources to produce and distribute goods and services.

An economic _____ is an organized way that a state, nation, or country manages all their production, buying, and selling.

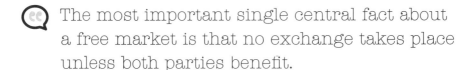

The most important single central fact about a free market is that no exchange takes place unless both parties benefit.

MILTON FRIEDMAN, American economist

FOUR PRIMARY ECONOMIC SYSTEMS

TRADITIONAL

Traditional economic systems are based on tradition. The work that people do, the things they make and sell, and their use of resources are based on the way things have been done for a long time. Each new generation continues the pattern. So, if your parents and grandparents made rugs or pottery, then you would be expected to do the same thing. Traditional economies generally have very little waste, but they also have very little extra, or surplus, left over. Rural and underdeveloped locations often operate with a traditional economy.

COMMAND

In a command system, a large part of the economy is controlled, or *commanded*, by a central power. This is often the government and can be seen in countries that practice communism or **socialism**. Here, the government owns, controls, and regulates all aspects of production, trade, and income generated by the most valuable resources. The government also regulates wages and the price of goods and services. The government commands all aspects related to surplus and distribution of goods and services.

MARKET

In this type of system, everything takes place within the "market"—where all kinds of things are sold, bought, and traded. The government is not involved in the activities related to the financial assets (or **capital**) used for business. This is referred to as **capitalism**. Individuals are completely in control of the resources, the production of goods and services, what jobs or training they will pursue, and what they will buy. The cost of goods and services is determined by supply and demand. In turn, buyers decide what goods and services they want and how much they are willing to pay for them. Capitalism is characterized by competition within the market.

MIXED

A mixed economic system is one that combines certain aspects of the other three systems. The United States operates with a capitalistic mindset within a mixed economic system. People are free to pursue whatever business they desire and choose the types of goods and services they want to offer the public with limited government regulation or interference. Consumers are free to determine what types of things they want to buy, as well as how much they are willing to pay. In turn, the government collects taxes to pay for a variety of programs and services including the postal service, education, the military, and other social services that benefit the public.

What would it be like if everyone had to shop at the same store or buy the same brand?

SUPPLY AND DEMAND

In a _____ economy, prices are based on how much people are willing to pay.

Prices go up and down based on the _____ of something and the _____ for it.

A market economy is driven by something referred to as "supply and demand." Consumers drive a market economy by choosing what to buy or not to buy—that's the "demand" part. Supply, on the other hand, is determined by the amount of resources available and the production of goods and services to be sold.

At higher prices, consumers will demand less. In response, companies may be willing to produce and supply more of an item, thus lowering their overall cost-per-item in order to get people to buy things. Competition is a major force driving supply and demand. If one company sells a good or service at a price that is too high, another company will sell a similar product for less money and sell more.

Companies want to sell things at the highest price possible; however, when prices become too high, people stop buying those things. That's because consumers want to buy things at the *lowest* price possible. But companies would not be able to stay in business if their prices are too low. In this way, a market economy regulates itself and should require little, if any, government involvement.

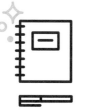

JOURNAL QUESTION

What evidence do you see around you that proves you are living in a market economy?

_____

_____

_____

_____

Making It to Market

In a market-based economy, money is used to buy a product.
Before something can be sold, however, it has to be made.
Here is how that happens.

1 A company creates a new design for a pair of shoes. They will purchase, from other companies, anything needed to make the shoes. This includes all the various materials and pieces, as well as any machines needed to make and package the shoes. The company makes money and pays their employees by selling their boxes of shoes to other stores.

The shoe manufacturer uses the money from the shoe store to buy more material to make more shoes. They would also use the money to pay the people who are making the shoes. The cycle would start again and continue as needed.

5

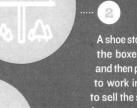

2 A shoe store pays for the boxes of shoes and then pays people to work in the store to sell the shoes. The shoe store also pays for some advertising and displays the shoes so people can try them on before they buy them.

4 The shoe store uses the money you paid for your shoes, along with money from other people's purchases, to pay business expenses—employees' wages, rent and utilities, and any advertising. They would also use the money to buy more shoes from the shoe manufacturer.

3 That is where you—the consumer—come in. You go to the shoe store, try on the shoes, and decide if the price is reasonable for those shoes. If it is, you pay for the shoes (using money you earned from babysitting or mowing yards) and take them home.

— APPLY WHAT YOU'VE LEARNED —

Pizza Time

You just opened a pizza shop targeting students at a local college. Pizza is one of the favorite food choices among college students. Your best seller is your signature pizza. It costs $4.25 to make. That price includes a $2 cost per pizza for the cheese, the most expensive ingredient. Add to that the costs of the dough, sauce, and toppings—$1.25. You also have other costs (rent, utilities, and employee wages) of about $1 per pizza.

DIRECTIONS: Using the information above and the scenarios below, complete the two calculations. Then respond to questions three and four.

1. You sell the signature pizza for $14. That means you make a profit of $8.75 for every pizza you sell. You normally sell 100 signature pizzas each week. How much profit would that be each week?

   $ _____

2. During mid-term testing week, your sales drop to 50 signature pizzas per week because the students are so busy studying for their tests. This means you would only make $437.50 in profit that week. You decide to try having a sale on the signature pizzas during testing week to increase sales. If you sold the signature pizzas for $11 each, and sold 120 of them, how much would you make in profit?

   $ _____

3. Does it make sense to reduce the price of your pizzas in order to boost sales? Why or why not?

   _____

   _____

4. How does this activity demonstrate the principles of supply and demand?

   _____

   _____

- -

FINAL THOUGHT: Hiram provided Solomon with all the cedar and cypress timber he wanted.

1 KINGS 5:10 HCSB

The Flow of Economics

A variety of factors can impact economic conditions.

ECONOMIC ACTIVITY

Economic activity happens, on some level, in every country. Economic activities are ways in which people make their livings. Depending on the economic development of a country, some activities will be more common than others. Here are a few terms related to economic activity:

Poverty is often described as a lack of financial resources. You will find people living in poverty all around the world, including the United States.

GDP stands for Gross Domestic Product. It is a measurement, in dollars, of a country's total goods and services.

Chain of Production is all the different steps needed to produce items so that you can go to the store and buy them.

THE CHAIN OF PRODUCTION

The movement of all the different goods and services is called the _____ of production.

Just about everything you use every day—from the clothes you wear to the cell phone you use to the books you read to the food you eat—flows through a chain of production within an economy.

A nation's economy is typically divided into sectors. A sector is simply an area of the economy that shares similar characteristics. There are four economic sectors that categorize economic activity.

The Chain of Production

THE FOUR ECONOMIC SECTORS

1 PRIMARY: Getting and refining raw materials from the earth (such as farming, fishing, forestry, and mining).

3 TERTIARY: Services to businesses and consumers (such as retail sales, restaurants, movies, banking, health care, and transportation).

2 SECONDARY: Processing raw materials into finished goods (such as making clothes, engineering cars and ships, and building homes and businesses).

4 QUATERNARY: Industries that process and distribute information (such as government, libraries, education, and information technology). These industries require the highest level of education.

Here's a quick example of how the chain of production works:

Potatoes are grown on a farmer's field and harvested, salt is mined, and plants are harvested for their seeds to become canola oil (**1**). Then the potatoes, salt, and seeds are processed and all the materials are sent to a company that turns them into potato chips and puts them in bags and then boxes them for delivery (**2**). The finished product is shipped to your favorite store where you can buy them (**3**).

Where is the fourth sector—the quaternary sector? Remember, it includes all kinds of intellectual activities and pursuits, including research and development. In the potato chip example, research and development departments create new flavors of potato chips within the production phase.

WHAT IS GDP?

> GDP stands for Gross Domestic Product and it's used to measure the size of a country's _____.

GDP represents the total of value of goods and services produced by a country each year. Countries with the highest GDP figures include the United States and China—the two largest—followed by Japan, Germany, France, and the United Kingdom. GDP is a good indicator of whether the economy in a country is growing or shrinking. Other economic indicators that can be used include the Consumer Price Index (CPI) (how much different things cost and the change in those prices), unemployment figures, and the price of crude oil.

> A country's GDP is an indication of the economic _____ of that country.

ECONOMIC DEVELOPMENT

There are a lot of different factors that influence the economic condition of a country. You will often hear countries described as developed or developing. "Developed" refers to the quality of a country's infrastructure like roads, water, electricity, and how well their marketplace operates. Examples include the United States, Canada, England, and France.

In contrast, a developing country—such as India, South Africa, Mexico, and the Philippines—does not have the same level of economic growth, business and industry, or security as the leading GDP countries. These countries generally have an agriculture-based economy, a higher population growth rate, and a higher level of unemployment.

% 80% of people in the US work in some sort of service-related job. (tertiary sector)

% 3% of people in the US work in jobs that extract or harvest products from the earth. (primary sector)[3]

> Poverty is often described as lacking the financial resources—money and ability to earn money—to meet a _____ standard of living in a society.
>
> 9

Poverty doesn't just happen in countries with few resources. The Census Bureau reports there are over 46 million Americans living in poverty.[4] But unlike some parts of the world, there are a lot more opportunities for people in the US who are living in poverty. When someone in the US says, "I'm poor," generally they mean they have no money or resources, which is what it means to be broke. Poor is a mindset; it's saying, "I'll never have anything." It isn't tied to your true financial state. Dave Ramsey often says, "I've been broke, but I've never been poor."

> _____ is temporary, but _____
> 10   11
> is a state of mind.

There are plenty of opportunities in the United States to work and to make money. You are learning about a lot of different financial principles and ideas that you can put into practice to help you change your behavior, to start thinking differently about money, and to stop spending money you don't have.

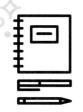

JOURNAL QUESTION

What kinds of things would be considered natural resources?

_____

_____

_____

_____

— APPLY WHAT YOU"VE LEARNED —

Getting to Market

You probably don't give much thought to all the steps required to make products you see displayed in your favorite stores. There are shelves of food products, racks of clothing, and aisles of electronics. It all comes through the chain of production.

DIRECTIONS: For each of the products identified in the right-hand column, list what would need to happen in the first three sectors of the chain of production before you would get to enjoy the product. The first one is completed for you.

Primary	Secondary	Tertiary	Product for you
Trees are cut down	The tree is chopped up and made into paper; then it's printed and bound into a book	The finished book is sold in a store	Your favorite book/mag
			A can of sliced pineapple
			A ring or bracelet
			A home
			A oar
			A baseball bat

FINAL THOUGHT: He has filled them with skill to do all manner of work of the engraver and the designer.

EXODUS 35:35 NKJV

Global Connections

World Stats

» Over **7.3 billion** world population

» **55.5 million** cars produced this year

» **109.8 million** bicycles produced this year

» **189.1 million** computers produced this year

» **1.3 billion** cell phones sold this year

Population Below Poverty Level

» **4–7**%: France, Switzerland, Austria, and Ireland

» **14–18**%: United States, China, Japan, Germany, United Kingdom

» **25–30**%: Argentina, Venezuela, Panama, Philippines

» **48–52**%: South Africa, Kenya, Mexico

» **70–80**%: Haiti, Chad, Liberia, Nigeria

Top US Imports

» Crude Oil **$356 billion**

» Machines/engines/pumps **$330 billion**

» Electronics/computers/cell phones **$319 billion**

» Vehicles **$265 billion**

» Medical/Technical equipment **$76 billion**

Top US Exports

» Machines/engines/pumps $219 billion

» Electronic equipment $172 billion

» Petroleum products $157 billion

» Vehicles $135 billion

» Aircraft, spacecraft $124 billion

Facebook Numbers

» **968 million** daily users worldwide

» **844 million** mobile users

» **1.49 billion** monthly active users

» **1 billion** people used Facebook in a single day (Aug. 24, 2015)

» **83**% of daily active users live outside of the US and Canada

Worldwide GDP Leaders

1. United States

2. China

3. Japan

4. Germany

5. United Kingdom

See Chapter 5 endnote source citations 5, 6, 7, 8, 9, 10.

Global Trade Activity

We can all work together in this global community.

LESSON 3

GLOBAL CONNECTIONS

We truly are a connected planet—and not just on social media. You're probably wearing clothes from different countries. You may have electronics that were made in Japan or China. You may eat food that comes from Ecuador, Guatemala, or Chile. You also buy a lot of stuff that is made or grown in the US. Some economic terms to understand include **globalization**, **interdependence**, and global trade.

Globalization describes different countries around the world _____ with each other.

Interdependence means _____ on other countries for resources, goods, or services.

Global trade happens between countries in the form of _____ and _____.

Countries send resources and goods they produce to other countries (export) while, at the same time, buying resources and goods from other countries (import). If a country does not have the natural resources or materials—or the manufacturing ability—to produce something, trade is a good thing. Trade provides the money to buy, and import, other goods. Imports and exports are beneficial for all parties.

What are some things you have with you right now that came from another country?

Having an advantage, especially related to global economics, refers to the ability of a country to produce something at a lower cost per unit (piece or item) than another country. Two examples of advantage are absolute advantage and comparative advantage. They both impact global trade and economics.

> Having an _____ advantage just means a company or country can produce a product at a lower cost than another country.

For example, if Country A can produce cell phones for a production cost of $400 each but Country B can produce cell phones for a production cost of $200 each, then Country B has the absolute advantage. They are the best at making cell phones and will make more profit.

When a country has a comparative advantage, it is able to produce a product at a lower cost than another country. So, absolute advantage is related to being more *cost effective* at producing something, but comparative advantage is related to being more *efficient* at production.

For example, if Country A can produce 1,000 denim jeans and 100 pairs of shoes per week, and Country B can produce 100 denim jeans and 1,000 pairs of shoes per week, both countries have the ability to produce jeans and shoes. However, Country A has a comparative advantage in jeans, while Country B has a comparative advantage in shoes. So, Country A could just make jeans—and make more of them. Country B could just make shoes—and make more of them. Both countries would then benefit by trading jeans for shoes and get more of the items than they could make themselves.

 Peace, commerce, and honest friendship with all nations—entangling alliances with none.

THOMAS JEFFERSON, Third President of the United States

THE IMPACT OF SCARCITY

Scarcity occurs when there is greater demand for something than what is actually available. A good example is clean drinking water. There are many populations around the world that struggle with water scarcity. In fact, according to the World Health Organization, four out of every ten people live where water is scarce or unsafe.[11] The lack of water kills more people around the world than AIDS, malaria, and all wars combined.

As a global community, we have the ability to work together to improve the management of resources—like providing access to clean drinking water for more people. In the area of water scarcity, such efforts have included protection of the environment, more equitable distribution of water, and rationing.

Rationing is a process to control the amount of goods or services being used. Sometimes this happens as the result of a natural disaster that leads to scarcity. For example, after Superstorm Sandy in 2012, some areas of New Jersey rationed gasoline because some fuel stations couldn't get any delivered and other stations had no electricity to pump it.

At other times, if the government fears there may be a shortage of something, they may ration it. For example, in some western US states where rainfall totals are often well below normal, water rationing may be necessary in order to limit the amount of water used. Often this means you can't wash a car, water a lawn, or use an excessive amount of water without financial penalties.

% 40% of the world population has Internet access— with over three billion Internet users worldwide.

% 48% of Internet users live in Asia; only 10% of Internet users live in North America.[12]

JOURNAL QUESTION

What kinds of connections, if any, do you have with the rest of the world?

_____

_____

_____

_____

— APPLY WHAT YOU"VE LEARNED —

The World in My House

As a result of the chain of production, as well as all the imports and exports that happen around the world, we use a lot of products from different countries. Most of us don't really stop to consider where all this stuff comes from. It's time to take a look around and see the world represented in the things you own.

DIRECTIONS: Take a look at some of the things you have in your home—food, clothing, electronics, shoes, and other items. Look around your house and in your room. Check out different food items in the kitchen. In this space, list where all the different things come from.

Item	Source(s)
Bananas	Honduras

FINAL THOUGHT: Solomon's horses were imported from Egypt and from Kue—the royal merchants purchased them from Kue at the current price. They imported a chariot from Egypt for six hundred shekels of silver, and a horse for a hundred and fifty.

1 KINGS 10:28–29 NIV

Recap & Review

WHAT CAN YOU DO NOW?

 It's time to check your learning! Go back to the "I Can" statements at the beginning of this chapter. Place a check mark next to each statement that you can do now.

ILLUSTRATION TIME

Draw a picture representation of the following terms.

Capitalism

Interdependence

SELF TEST

Circle the correct answer.

1. **An economic system in which the government owns, controls, and regulates all aspects of production, trade, and income generated by the most valuable resources is called a _____ economy.**
   Ⓐ Market   Ⓑ Traditional   Ⓒ Mixed   Ⓓ Command

2. **An economic system based on the private ownership of business and the products made and sold is called a _____ economy**
   Ⓐ Command   Ⓑ Market   Ⓒ Traditional   Ⓓ Mixed

3. **In which of the economic sectors are raw materials turned into finished products?**
   Ⓐ Primary   Ⓑ Tertiary   Ⓒ Secondary   Ⓓ Quaternary

4. **The monetary value of all goods and services produced in a country in a year is called**
   Ⓐ Currency   Ⓒ Industry product
   Ⓑ Supply and demand   Ⓓ Gross domestic product

5. **The interaction between the various countries of the world is called**
   Ⓐ Friendship   Ⓒ Interdependence
   Ⓑ Globalization   Ⓓ Business

6. **The reliance of one country on the resources, goods, or services of another country is called**
   Ⓐ Interdependence   Ⓒ Globalization
   Ⓑ Supply and demand   Ⓓ Scarcity

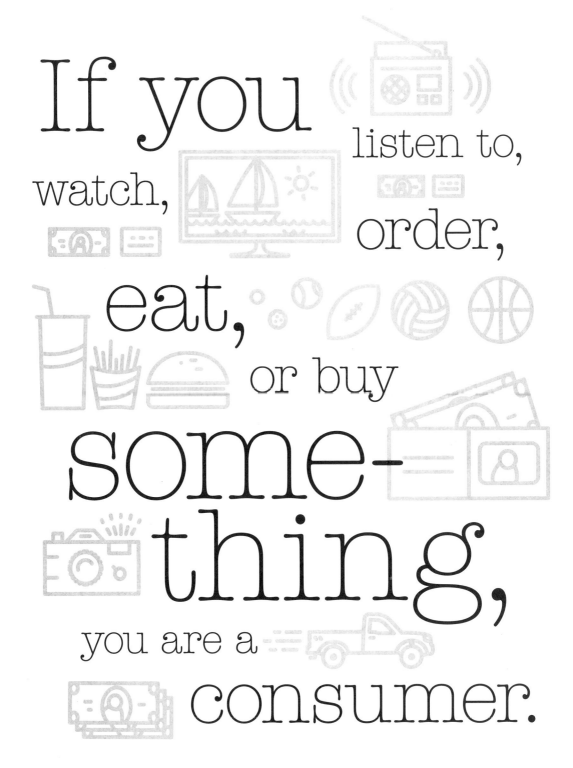

If you watch, listen to, order, eat, or buy something, you are a consumer.

06

Marketing & Consumerism

Be a wise spender.

81% of teen girls say they rely on their friends and peers to discover the latest trends.[1]

71% of students have "liked" a brand on social media to receive an offer.[2]

> Marketing is about values. It's a complicated and noisy world, and we're not going to get a chance to get people to remember much about us.

STEVE JOBS, entrepreneur, marketer, and inventor

> Without promotion, something terrible happens . . . nothing!

P.T. BARNUM, founder of Barnum and Bailey Circus

> Discretion will protect you, and understanding will guard you.

PROVERBS 2:11 NIV

I Can...

☑ At the end of this chapter, come back to this list and mark the things you understand and could explain to a friend.

LESSON 1

☐ Recognize the ways companies compete for my money.

☐ Describe how peer pressure influences spending choices.

☐ Define marketing.

LESSON 2

☐ Define contentment.

☐ Explain the concept of economic incentives.

☐ Analyze and evaluate the claims in advertising.

LESSON 3

☐ Understand the role of the FTC.

☐ Explain bait and switch.

☐ Describe some ways to be a wise consumer.

💬 For where your treasure is, there your heart will be also.

MATTHEW 6:21 NKJV

Key Terms

Get to know the language of money.

Bait and Switch: Advertising a lower priced item to lure customers in to offer them a more expensive item

Brand Loyalty: Buying decisions based on preference to always purchase a certain type of product from a particular brand

Contentment: The state of being satisfied with what you have

FTC / Federal Trade Commission: The main federal agency designed to enforce consumer protection laws

Fraudulent: Intentionally false or deceptive practices

Impulse Purchase: An unplanned, spur of the moment, purchase generally sparked by advertising and emotion

Incentives: Something that motivates or encourages someone to do something; coupons or special offers from a company to entice you to buy something

Marketing: Everything a company does to get consumers to buy their product

Photoshopping: Digitally changing/enhancing a photograph to make it look better than the actual item

Product Placement: The paid display of specific products (food, drinks, clothing, and identifiable brands) in movies, television, and media for advertisement

Buyer Beware

It's important to become wise consumers.

SPENDING HABITS

Buying stuff can be fun! Walk into any store or mall and you are surrounded with so many different things you could buy. What are some of the things that catch your eye? What do you buy with your money? How do you compare to other teenagers who are also out buying stuff? According to surveys, clothing and food (including specialty coffees) share first place at or just over 20% of the total amount of money spent by teens.[3]

Why are the spending habits of teens so important—and who really cares? Actually, businesses do care about what kinds of things you spend your money on. Based on the things you typically buy, companies will create ads specifically targeted to you. These ads make you feel as if the companies are talking directly to you and know all about your wants and needs. With all of this going on, it is important to learn to be a smart shopper.

 What is your favorite thing you bought recently? Why?

COMPETING FOR CASH

There are so many things you can buy, but you only have so much money and you can't buy everything (even if you wanted to). Companies know this. That is why they spend a lot of money on **marketing**. And that includes all of the ads you see

repeated over and over. Repetition is one of the powerful marketing tactics used by companies. When they can get you to remember the ad and product slogan, they have planted a marketing image in your brain.

How Teens Spend Their Money

According to a Piper Jaffray survey, teenagers spend as much money on food and drinks as they do on clothing. Here's a look at the overall breakdown of teen spending:

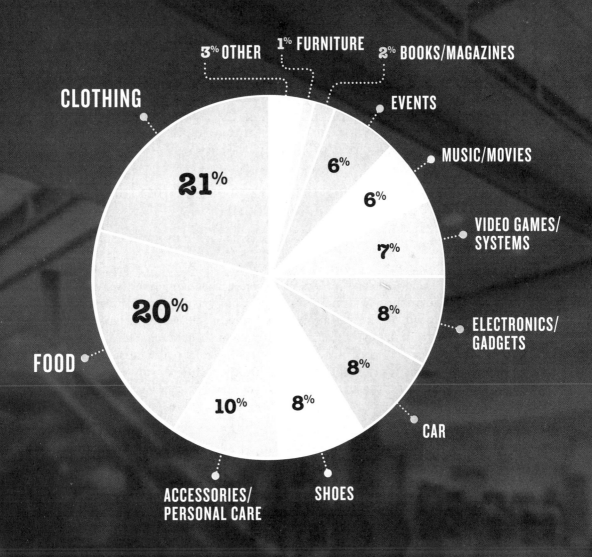

3% OTHER
1% FURNITURE
2% BOOKS/MAGAZINES
EVENTS
CLOTHING
MUSIC/MOVIES
21%
6%
6%
7%
VIDEO GAMES/SYSTEMS
8%
ELECTRONICS/GADGETS
20%
8%
CAR
FOOD
10%
8%
ACCESSORIES/PERSONAL CARE
SHOES

COMPETING FOR CASH (CONTINUED)

_____ is all of the things a company will do to promote their product.

When a company pays to market their product or service, they are trying to get you to buy their product or service instead of a similar item from another company. Actually, marketing is all around you. Names, logos, and labels are on everything. And, for a lot of people, those names and labels turn into **brand loyalty**. Have you ever heard someone say, "I will only buy 'this brand' of cell phone or 'that brand' of computer"? Consumers develop a lot of their brand loyalties during their teen years, and that is why so much advertising is targeted toward teens.

_____ _____ is often built through clever advertising and powerful marketing.

Another form of advertising is called product _____.

Product placement happens when a company pays money—a lot of money—to a movie or television show to make sure the characters will drink a certain type of drink, eat a certain type of food, wear certain types of clothing, or buy certain things. The company or product names are clearly displayed. The idea is that if you see an actor drinking, eating, wearing, or buying a certain type of thing, then you will be more likely to do the same. We have all purchased things as a result of product placement. When was the last time you bought something because your favorite celebrity endorses it or uses it? So, the next time you watch a movie or your favorite show on television, look for examples of product placement.

 Marketing is a contest for people's attention.

SETH GODIN, speaker and entrepreneur

CHOOSING WHAT TO BUY

There are a lot of factors that go into deciding what you are going to buy. But the most important factor according to teens, especially teen girls, is what their friends and peers think.[5] For example, if your best friend really likes a certain brand of clothing or shoes, chances are pretty good that you will like—and purchase—that same brand. That's what companies hope will happen.

> It's amazing how much _____
>
> _____ and the stuff our friends have
>
> affect what we want.

Another type of peer pressure comes from social media. Between all the different sites, there are almost 2 billion photos uploaded every day![6] And a bunch of those photos show people (your friends) promoting things they really like—candy, a fancy dessert, or a new article of clothing.

Sometimes we may find ourselves just staring at all the pictures of things we don't have, and, before we know it, we really want those things. And all of that promotion on social media is just free marketing for the companies that are trying to sell you their products.

> You can't let what _____ around you have
>
> affect how you feel about yourself.

JOURNAL QUESTION

What is something you bought recently because of brand loyalty, product placement, or peer pressure?

_____

_____

_____

_____

— APPLY WHAT YOU'VE LEARNED —

High-Priced Ads

A well-produced and well-placed ad for a product can lead to a lot of profit in sales depending on the number of consumers who buy something as a result of watching the ad. That's why companies are willing to spend millions of dollars to put an ad in the middle of your favorite show or sporting event.

DIRECTIONS: Using the information below, calculate the profits for a company presenting a product ad during a huge, televised sporting event.

A thirty-second commercial during the big football game at the end of every NFL season costs a lot of money. In 2015, a thirty-second ad cost $4.5 million. If you divide $4,500,000 by thirty, that works out to $150,000 per second![7]

Is the cost of a commercial worth it? Let's see. While $4.5 million is a lot of money, here is the way advertisers view it: It was estimated that 114.4 million people watched the big game in 2015. That would be 114.4 million potential customers watching your ad. If the commercial was really well done and funny, it might lead people to buy a product the next week. Companies compete to create the best ad because it will continue to be replayed on social media (tor tree) for weeks after the game. That is a bunch of free advertising for the company.

Let's say the company's product—maybe some sort of energy drink—sells for $1.69. It would seem rather foolish to spend $4.5 million on a product that only sells for $1.69 . . . until you do the math. Check it out:

1. How much would the company make if everyone who watched the commercial bought their product?

   (114,400,000 x $1.69) = $ _____

2. What if only half of the people watching bought their product?

   (57,200,000 x $1.69) = $ _____

3. What if only 25% of the people watching the ad bought the product?

   (28,600,000 x $1.69) = $ _____

4. What if only 10% of the people bought the product?

   (11,440,000 x $1.69) = $ _____

5. So, was it a good investment? YES / NO

   Why? _____

   _____

- -

FINAL THOUGHT: He who is impulsive exalts folly.

PROVERBS 14:29 NKJV

Masters of Marketing

Contentment is being satisfied with what you have.

IT'S BOGO TIME!

BOGO deals—or Buy One Get One Free deals—are great! Who doesn't love getting things for free? This is an example of an **incentive**. Coupons are another example. Say you went to the store and you weren't planning on spending seventy-five cents on a candy bar, but you found a coupon for twenty-five cents off that candy bar. Sure, you got a deal, but the company also got you to spend fifty cents that you weren't planning to spend because you felt like you were getting a good deal.

> _____ are things that companies use to get you to spend money.

Some common examples of economic incentives include:

» Buy One Get One Free offers (BOGO)

» Coupons and rebate offers

» Customer loyalty reward cards

» Store email with special deals for "select" customers

» Big sales (such as Black Friday)

» An extra 15% off if you use a store credit card

» Internet, phone, or email coupons

» Referral incentives (tell three friends and get yours free)

What is something that you want to buy right now because of an ad you saw on TV or online?

_____

Advertising Stats

Advertising is all around us. Some research indicates that the average American is exposed to over 4,000 advertisements every day—and not just on television or radio. Consider these figures:

Average daily number of hours:

4.3 WATCHING TELEVISION **2.8** ON A MOBILE DEVICE **2.4** ON A COMPUTER **2.0** LISTENING TO MUSIC

Average minutes of commercials in one hour of programming:

15 Min. WATCHING TELEVISION **12 Min.** LISTENING TO THE RADIO

Average number of commercials:

30 COMMERCIALS PER HOUR ON TV = **129** COMMERCIALS PER DAY (AVG.) = **47,085** COMMERCIALS PER YEAR (AVG.)

24 COMMERCIALS PER HOUR ON RADIO = **48** COMMERCIALS PER DAY (AVG.) = **17,520** COMMERCIALS PER YEAR (AVG.)

Televised Football

The average NFL game includes about **20** commercial breaks and an average of **100** ads. And that doesn't include all the name and logo branding on everything you see on the broadcast.

Advertising impressions are made every time you:

» brush your teeth and see the brand of toothpaste and toothbrush

» put on your clothes and shoes

» get into your car

» open your refrigerator or pantry and see all the labels

» drive past places to eat

» see billboards and advertising along the road

See Chapter 6 endnote source citations 8, 9, 10, 11, 12.

A MATERIALISTIC SOCIETY

Stuff is not going to make you happy. That is an important truth to understand considering we live in the most marketed-to culture in the world. Face it: companies are competing to get you to buy their goods. And when you don't buy the things they are selling, their ads often make you feel left out. Those ads make you feel like you are not satisfied unless you have "X" and they make you think your life will be so much better if you go buy it. That is called discontentment.

> Contentment is being _____ with what you already have.

Contentment is a powerful financial principle. Content people are satisfied with the perfectly good pair of shoes they have, and they know that buying another pair of shoes is not going to make them really happy. For example, you can be content eating a hamburger even though a big steak sounds pretty good.

> There is a way for you to become content, and that is first to become _____.

Being grateful requires being thankful. Take the time to express your thankfulness to others. When you say "thank you," mean it. Being grateful also relates to your wants and needs. Ask yourself, *Do I really need this?* and *How much is enough for me?* Being content with what you have will keep you from spending money you don't have and going into debt for something you don't really need.

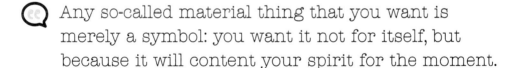
Any so-called material thing that you want is merely a symbol: you want it not for itself, but because it will content your spirit for the moment.

MARK TWAIN, author

HEY! WAIT A MINUTE!

We buy a lot of stuff as _____ purchases.

The goal of advertising is to get your attention and lead you to do something—to buy some gum, a hamburger or burrito, a particular brand of cereal, or even toothpaste. Just about everything is marketed to us to catch our attention. These ads work. We buy a lot of stuff. In fact, 75% of adults surveyed said they have made **impulse purchases**.[13]

One of the practices of a wise consumer is to evaluate the claims made in an ad. Will this product be the best thing you have ever tasted? Probably not. Will the product instantly surround you with all kinds of new friends? Probably not. Will the product make you smarter, prettier, faster, taller, or something else? Probably not. It is up to you, as the consumer, to evaluate the claims of each product. Remember, marketers try to influence your emotions to get you to buy stuff.

You're probably familiar with the "**photoshopping**" effect—just about everything you see in ads has been altered on a computer and made to look better than it really does. For example, when was the last time you bought a hamburger, taco, or any other fast-food item that looked as good in person as it did in the ad or on the menu?

Did you know that many of the food photos you see are actually created by a food designer (or food stylist) who gets paid to make food look really good? Sometimes they use plastic models of food, or the food is carefully photographed and then digitally enhanced. Other tricks include using hairspray to make food look fresh, using motor oil to simulate syrup or honey, or using colored mashed potatoes in place of ice cream, because mashed potatoes don't melt and they hold their shape.

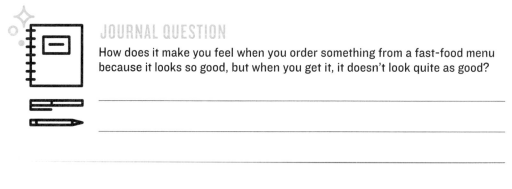

JOURNAL QUESTION

How does it make you feel when you order something from a fast-food menu because it looks so good, but when you get it, it doesn't look quite as good?

_____

_____

—— APPLY WHAT YOU'VE LEARNED ——

Getting a Deal

Being able to quickly figure out the savings of the sales at your favorite stores is important. Everyone is looking for a deal—but is it really a good deal?

DIRECTIONS: Calculate the final cost for the following items.

1. 20% off an item priced at $9.99

   $_____

   Hint: A quick way to figure the approximate savings in your head while in a store is to use a 10% calculation. For the first example, the item is almost $10. And 10% of $10 is $1. So since this is a 20% off sale, you would save about $2 off the price.

2. A shirt retails for $29.99, but it is marked down to $12.50 on a sales rack with a sign reading "Take an additional 30% off the sale price." What is the final cost?

   $_____

   Hint: Using the same idea for the second example, you need to figure the approximate extra savings from the $12.50 sale price. So 10% of $12.50 is $1.25. And since the savings are an extra 30% off, that would be 3 x $1.25 for an extra savings of $3.75.

3. 75% off an item priced at $44.95

   $_____

   Hint: For the third example, a quick way to figure the price of something marked 75% off is to divide the price by 4 (4 x 25% is 100%).

4. Buy one pair of shoes at regular price and get the second pair (of equal or lesser value) at 50% off. You find a pair for $49 and another pair for $69. What is your final cost?

   $_____

   Hint: The $49 pair of shoes would be the discounted pair. You can also use 50% (half) off for quick calculations, which is just dividing a price by 2. For example, in this last example, the $49 shoes would be 50% off. 50% of $49 is $24.50 (49 / 2 = 24.5).

- -

FINAL THOUGHT: Happy is the man who finds wisdom, and the man who gains understanding.

PROVERBS 3:13 NKJV

You Have Rights

As a consumer, you're protected from being ripped off.

YOU'RE PROTECTED

As a consumer, you buy and use a lot of stuff. And, honestly, sometimes we all buy things we don't need; sometimes it's just junk. So, what are you supposed to do if after you buy a new backpack, you get home and discover that one of the zippers is broken? Are you just supposed to live with it? Or maybe you pick out a great T-shirt that has a medium "M" label, but when you get home to try it on, it definitely fits like an extra-small. What can you do about that? There are laws put in place to protect you and your rights as a consumer. When you buy stuff and it doesn't work, doesn't fit, or is missing parts, you have the right as a consumer to get a refund or to get the item fixed or replaced.

> The FTC is the Federal _____ Commission and their job is to enforce the laws to protect consumers.

The **FTC** protects consumers by stopping unfair, deceptive, or **fraudulent** practices in the marketplace. The FTC will also investigate companies to make sure they are not breaking the law. They also educate consumers about their rights and responsibilities. As a consumer, you have the right to submit a complaint to the FTC to report any unfair business practices that you encounter.

 When have you regretted buying something? Why?

Bait and Switch

The "**bait and switch**" trick is an illegal scam to get your money. For example, a company might advertise something at a super low price to get you to come to the store so you can purchase the item. However, when you get there and ask about the advertised deal (the bait)—surprise!—they are completely out of the item. Instead, they offer to sell you a similar, but more expensive, product (the switch). This is an act of fraud.

DEALING WITH PROBLEMS

No matter how carefully you research and plan your purchases, eventually you will end up with a product that has some sort of problem. It could be anything from the quality of the product to missing parts to the item breaking easily. So, what do you do when you run into one of these problems or any other problem?

> The Federal Trade Commission suggests some things you can do to resolve a _____.
>
> ₁₁

The most important factor in dealing with a problem is to use a reasonable tone and explain your problem clearly. Yelling, screaming, and getting angry won't help you resolve the situation any faster. Here are some ideas:

» **Return the item.** Many problems can be resolved if you return the item to the store or contact the company if you ordered it online. This should be done as soon as you discover a problem. Keep a record of when you talk to someone.

» **Call the customer service department.** Ask to speak to a supervisor. If you bought an item online, you can often find a "Contact Us" link to communicate a problem. You can also post a comment on social media. Make sure to use a reasonable tone and clearly state the problem.

» **Write a letter.** Clearly describe the problem and state how you would like the problem resolved. Don't be angry, sarcastic, or threatening. Make sure to include your phone number and address so the company can contact you.

» **Use state and federal agencies.** If a phone call or a letter doesn't help you resolve the problem, you can contact an agency to help you. The Better Business Bureau, the FTC, and other organizations can provide assistance in resolving complaints you may have with a company or product.

 Just as consumers have the right to know what is in their credit contract, so also do they have the right to know what is in the package they buy.

JOHN F. KENNEDY, thirty-fifth president of the United States

Common Consumer Problems

It is not uncommon to have a problem with something you buy. It happens to everyone. Here is a quick look at some of the stats and information related to these problems:

The Five Major Types of Complaints

1. **Performance/Operation:** defective, broken, non-working items; missing parts; wrong size

2. **Customer Touch Points:** behavior, attitude, performance, billing issues with employees/administration

3. **Marketing:** misleading ads, brand didn't deliver on promises

4. **Business/Company Service:** complaints related to flaws, deficiencies, negligence, or problems with a business/company

5. **False Complaints:** false postings of poor service or negative reviews posted just to be mean

In a recent national survey related to customer complaints, There were 2.5 million complaints registered.

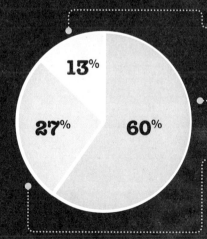

Identity Theft Related (325,000)
e.g. driver's license, Social Security numbers, personal information misused, government documents/benefits fraud

Fraud Related (1.5 Million)
e.g. debt collection, email/phone scams, auto related, health care fraud

'Other' Types Of Complaints (675,000)
e.g. shop at home issues, television and electronics issues, internet services, telephones and mobile services, computer equipment and software, home repair and improvement products

See Chapter 6 endnote source citations 14, 15.

BE A WISE CONSUMER

It's easy to spend more money than you make because credit is such an _____ _____.

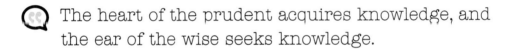

Here are some great ideas to help you practice being a wise consumer, especially when you are considering a bigger purchase.

» Research the item before you buy it, and search for a better deal. Consider if the item is really worth the price.

» Wait overnight before making a big purchase. Think about why you really want the item.

» Talk with your parent or another adult about your decision.

» Make sure you have the money, and always pay cash.

" The heart of the prudent acquires knowledge, and the ear of the wise seeks knowledge.

PROVERBS 18:15 NKJV

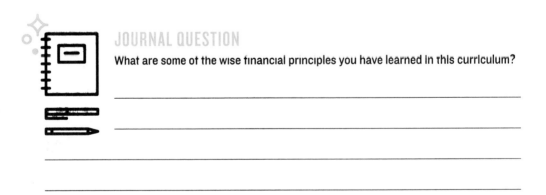

JOURNAL QUESTION

What are some of the wise financial principles you have learned in this curriculum?

_____

_____

_____

_____

— APPLY WHAT YOU'VE LEARNED —

Misleading Ads

You see a lot of ads every day. Companies are always looking for new ways to describe their products to catch your attention and get you to buy something.

DIRECTIONS: Read each of the following advertising messages. In the space below each statement, describe what is false or misleading about the ad.

1. X-ray Glasses. The greatest invention of the century. Can see bones through skin and lead through pencils. Fantastic!

   _____

   _____

2. Carb Blocker and Fat Blocker Pills. The easy way to lose weight while eating what you want.

   _____

   _____

3. Miracle TV Box. Never pay for cable again. Get all the channels you want for free.

   _____

   _____

4. White Plus Toothpaste. Teeth so white your friends will need sunglasses.

   _____

   _____

5. Wrinkles Be Gone. Visibly reduces years of wrinkles in only a few minutes.

   _____

   _____

- -

FINAL THOUGHT: Dishonest scales are an abomination to the Lord, but a just weight is His delight.

PROVERBS 11:1 NKJV

Recap & Review

WHAT CAN YOU DO NOW?

 It's time to check your learning! Go back to the "I Can" statements at the beginning of this chapter. Place a check mark next to each statement that you can do now.

ILLUSTRATION TIME

Draw a picture representation of the following terms.

Marketing

Contentment

SELF TEST

Circle the correct answer.

1. On which of the following do teens spend the most money?
- **Ⓐ** Clothing and food
- **Ⓑ** Accessories (such as jewelry)
- **Ⓒ** Electronics
- **Ⓓ** Entertainment

2. Which of the following is an example of an economic incentive?
- **Ⓐ** Debit card purchase
- **Ⓑ** Inflation
- **Ⓒ** Buying something for a friend
- **Ⓓ** Online sales or discounts

3. The federal agency designed to enforce consumer protection laws
- **Ⓐ** Federal Deposit Insurance Corporation
- **Ⓑ** North American Free Trade Agreement
- **Ⓒ** Federal Trade Commission
- **Ⓓ** Securities Exchange Commission

4. A person who buys things is called a(n)
- **Ⓐ** Worker
- **Ⓑ** Consumer
- **Ⓒ** Entrepreneur
- **Ⓓ** Merchant

5. Something that motivates or encourages someone to do something
- **Ⓐ** Buyer's remorse
- **Ⓑ** Supply and demand
- **Ⓒ** Contentment
- **Ⓓ** Incentives

6. _____ is being satisfied with what you already have.
- **Ⓐ** Brand loyalty
- **Ⓑ** Contentment
- **Ⓒ** Marketing
- **Ⓓ** Consumerism

Endnotes

A complete list of source citations is available on the Digital Teacher's Edition.

CHAPTER 1

1. Daniel P. Ray and Yasmin Ghahremani, "Credit Card Statistics, Industry Facts, Debt Statistics," CreditCards.com.
2. Ibid.
3. Charles Schwab, "2011 Teens & Money Survey Findings."
4. Ibid.
5. Shirley Leung and Ron Lieber, "The New Menu Option at McDonald's: Plastic," *Wall Street Journal*.
6. Daniel P. Ray and Yasmin Ghahremani, "Credit Card Statistics, Industry Facts, Debt Statistics," CreditCards.com.
7. Ibid.
8. Charles Schwab, "2011 Teens & Money Survey Findings."
9. SaveUp.com, "Surprising Finding: Young People Are Aggressively Saving."
10. Piper Jaffray, "Taking Stock With Teens" 28th Annual Survey.

CHAPTER 2

1. Tamara E. Holmes and Yasmin Ghahremani, "Credit Card Statistics," CreditCards.com.
2. Ibid.
3. Extrapolated from various sources.
4. Charles Schwab, "Teens & Money" Survey.
5. CreditCards.com, Minimum Payment Calculator.
6. *U.S. News and World Report*, "Average Student Loan Debt Approaches $30,000."
7. Charles Schwab, "2011 Teens & Money Survey Findings."
8. Ibid.

CHAPTER 3

1. JA—ING Direct, "Teens and Careers" Survey.
2. Ibid.
3. *U.S. News and World Report*, "Best Jobs 2015."
4. College Board, "Education Pays" Study.
5. Jason Nazar, "16 Surprising Statistics About Small Businesses," *Forbes*.
6. The 2013 Gallup–Hope Index.

CHAPTER 4

1. TermLifeFinancial, "The Importance of Insurance Shown Through Statistics."
2. Charles Schwab, "2011 Teens & Money Survey Findings."
3. Adam Shell, "Holding stocks for 20 years can turn bad returns to good," *USA Today*.
4. Guard Child, "Identity Theft Statistics."
5. Kimberly Rotter, "The Staggering Cost of Identity Theft in the U.S.," Credit Sesame.

CHAPTER 5

1. Mark Fischetti, "U.S. Demand for Fruits and Vegetables Drives Up Imports," Scientific American.

2. United Nations, "Vital Statistics: Hunger."

3. Matt Rosenberg, "Sectors of the Economy," About Education.

4. Shirley Leung and Ron Lieber, "The New Menu Option at McDonald's: Plastic," *The Wall Street Journal*.

5. Worldometers, "Population."

6. CIA World Factbook, "Population Below Poverty Line," Index Mundi.

7. World's Richest Countries, "Top US Imports."

8. World's Richest Countries, "Top US Exports."

9. Facebook Newsroom, "Company Info."

10. The World Bank, "GDP Ranking."

11. World Health Organization, "Water, Sanitation, and Health."

12. Internet Live Stats, "Internet Users."

CHAPTER 6

1. Statistic Brain Research Institute, "Teenage Consumer Spending Statistics."

2. Mr. Youth, "The New College Orientation."

3. Piper Jaffray, "Taking Stock with Teens Survey 2014."

4. Ibid.

5. Statistic Brain Research Institute, "Teenage Consumer Spending Statistics."

6. Naina Khedekar, "Meeker Internet Report," Tech 2.

7. Lindsay Kramer, "Super Bowl 2015," Syracuse Media Group.

8. Danyl Bosomworth, "Mobile Marketing Statistics 2015," SmartInsights.com.

9. Joe Flint, "Commercial Real Estate," *The Wall Street Journal*.

10. Thomas Giger, "How to Program Radio Commercial Breaks Strategically," Radio: I Love It.

11. Ron Marshall, "How Many Ads Do You See in One Day," Red Crow Marketing.

12. Zachary M. Seward, "An Average NFL Game," Quartz.

13. Martin Merzer, "Survey: 3 in 4 Americans make impulse purchases," CreditCards.com.

14. Easy Marketing A2Z, "Customer Complaints: Five Major Types That You Must Know."

15. Federal Trade Commission, "Sentinel Network Data Book 2014."

Let's make it official!

Student Achievement Certificate

Now that you've learned the key principles taught in Foundations in Personal Finance, *you can earn a personalized Certificate of Achievement recognizing your accomplishment!*

TO GET YOUR CERTIFICATE

1. Go to **foundationsU.com/middle-school** and click on "Get Certified."

2. Complete a randomized twenty-question quiz that will test your knowledge of the principles discussed in the *Foundations in Personal Finance* curriculum. Don't overthink this! All of the questions will be based on the information you learned.

3. After you pass the quiz with a score of 80% or higher, you'll get a personalized Certificate of Achievement ready for you to download and print so you can save it or share it with your parents or teacher.

CERTIFICATE
OF ACHIEVEMENT

This certifies that

Your Name

HAS SUCCESSFULLY PROVEN HIS/HER UNDERSTANDING OF THE DAVE RAMSEY PRINCIPLES
PRESENTED IN **FOUNDATIONS IN PERSONAL FINANCE: MIDDLE SCHOOL EDITION**
COMPLETED ON JANUARY 23, 2016

JIM KING
SENIOR VICE PRESIDENT, RAMSEY SOLUTIONS

DAVE RAMSEY
CEO, RAMSEY SOLUTIONS